From the Podium:
BP's Macondo Blowout

Based on

The Simple Truth:
BP's Macondo Blowout

Previously published:

J. A. Turley

The Simple Truth:
BP's Macondo Blowout

2012

Narrative nonfiction about the *cause* of the 2010 disaster aboard the Transocean *Deepwater Horizon* in the Gulf of Mexico. See Addendum 1 for description and access.

From the Podium:
BP's Macondo Blowout

Nonfiction

by

J. A. Turley

The Brier Patch, LLC
Littleton, Colorado, USA

Published by:
The Brier Patch, LLC
P.O. Box 184, Littleton, CO 80160-0184, USA

ISBN-13: 978-0-9858772-3-1 (paperback)
ISBN-13: 978-0-9858772-5-5 (ebook)

This is a work of nonfiction based on a true incident—BP's 2010 Macondo Blowout in the Gulf of Mexico aboard the Transocean *Deepwater Horizon* drilling rig. Information and diagrams used throughout have been extracted from the author's data-driven book *The Simple Truth: BP's Macondo Blowout* (published in 2012). Public data about companies, equipment, the well, and the rig, though modified by the author for ease of reading, form the basis for the work. Opinions are the author's.

Editing by Thomas N. Locke, with my sincere thanks.

Acknowledgements

I researched and wrote for two years before publishing *The Simple Truth: BP's Macondo Blowout* in September 2012. Soon thereafter, an energy company invited me to present my research findings in Houston, Texas. That successful event opened the way for me to make dozens of technical and keynote presentations around the world. Those presentations form the basis for this publication, *From the Podium.*

My sincere thanks go to each entity and host who welcomed my message, including Colorado School of Mines, Marietta College, Murphy ExP, Marathon Oil Company, the Society of Petroleum Engineers (SPE) in Houston, the Evangeline (Lafayette, Louisiana) Sierra Club, University of Louisiana at Lafayette, Louisiana State University, NETL/DOE, Chevron, Offshore Process Safety Conference, SPE Dallas, University of Oklahoma, Tulsa University, LAGCOE, SPE Mid-Continent, NPR Tulsa, Pennsylvania State University, West Virginia University, Southern Ohio Oilman's Association, IADC/SPE Dallas, Lafayette Geological Society, American Association of Drilling Engineers, Montana Tech University, University of Leoben Austria, Decom World, SPE Amsterdam, and Encana Services Company.

After almost fifty such presentations, I was invited to be an SPE Distinguished Lecturer (DL) for 2015-2016 and to make my presentation (same topic) to SPE sections on a global basis.

I am especially grateful to the thirty SPE sections and their volunteer leaders who hosted me during my travels to St. John's, Newfoundland and Labrador; Boston, Massachusetts; Washington, DC; Canton, Ohio; Lansing, Michigan; Traverse City, Michigan; Tyler, Texas; Hobbs, New Mexico; Texas A&M University; SPE Denver; Bahrain; Abu Dhabi, UAE; Dubai, UAE; London, England; Aberdeen, Scotland; Great Yarmouth, England; Madrid, Spain; Lloydminster, Alberta, Canada; San Ramon, California; Bartlesville, Oklahoma; Duncan, Oklahoma; Lafayette, Louisiana; and Tuscaloosa, Alabama.

I finished my tour with a trip to Perth, Australia; Adelaide, Australia; Melbourne, Australia; New Plymouth, New Zealand; Sydney, Australia; and then to Brisbane, Australia, where I made my last SPE-DL presentation on May 19, 2016.

For Jan

Forever my love,
my best friend,
and always my CFOOE

Contents

Introduction

On April 20, 2010, the major London-based energy company BP plc was blasted into the headlines by a disastrous blowout in the Gulf of Mexico aboard a deep-water drilling rig named *Deepwater Horizon.*

At the time, I had retired from my engineering and management career in oil and gas and had started a new venture—writing fiction. My learning curve was steep, but I won a couple of contests and wrote four novels. In the middle of drafting my fifth book, I heard about the hours-old catastrophe in the Gulf, the thought of which threatened to consume me. I immediately quit writing and focused on the disaster.

Why? Because that tragic event led to what I've now long described as *one of the most lethal, costly, manmade environmental disasters in history*, which will forever be known in the industry as *BP's Macondo Blowout.* But because the blowout took place aboard Transocean's *Deepwater Horizon* drilling rig, the media addressed the disaster as BP's *Deepwater Horizon* blowout and oil spill. In fact, the 2016 Hollywood film about the tragedy is named, simply: *Deepwater Horizon.*

A *blowout* is defined as the loss of control of a drilled well, wherein naturally occurring formation fluids—oil, gas, and water from sediments thousands of feet below the seafloor—flow into the drilled well and to the surface without control. Further, *Macondo* is BP's chosen nickname for the deep geologic structure targeted by the exploration well; hence, it was called the "Macondo well," and, without ambiguity, "BP's Macondo blowout."

BP's Macondo blowout killed eleven men. Further, the half-billion-dollar *Deepwater Horizon* burned, capsized, and sank in the mile-deep

Gulf. An estimated five million barrels (200 million gallons) of crude oil spilled into the Gulf during a media feeding frenzy that lasted eighty-six days. The cleanup operation, using a toxic dispersant, hid the floating crude oil but put the Gulf in jeopardy for years to come. Costs skyrocketed, eclipsing $60 billion—pushed by failed businesses, open-ocean cleanup, coastline and estuary rejuvenation, and litigation-related fines and penalties that, as of 2018, do not yet include the results of ongoing civil trials.

So, where do I, John Turley, fit in? Offshore operations, and drilling operations in general, occupied much of my professional career. In retirement, I was the neighborhood "oil guy," which led family and friends—inundated by TV and internet news—to ask, "John, what happened to that rig in the Gulf?"

My inability to answer that single question led me to give up fiction writing and start digging. I returned to the world of research and gathered publicly available data wherever I could find it. I listened to and reviewed thousands of pages of United States Coast Guard depositions, investigative reports, engineering procedures, published studies, and court transcripts. The more I looked for and found hard data, the more hooked I became at filling in the blanks and completing the puzzle as to what caused the blowout.

During the interim, as the media continued to saturate the listening/watching/reading world with the best information they'd gleaned from pontificating experts who often had vested interests, I made a two-part decision.

First, I committed myself to ignoring finger-pointing, politics, opinion, he-said-she-said, oily beaches, media headlines, court findings, company cultures, journalists, attorneys, and—albeit with great difficulty—the people involved, whether victims, survivors, or associated leaders.

Second, I would focus on only one thing—hard data. Specifically, I would gather available engineering and operating data from the rig and from the well that had been captured by the entities involved. The data would tell me the story I needed to know. It's the kind of story engineers can put to good use when working to help minimize the chance of ever losing control of another well.

My mantra, while gathering data and since, has been and remains: *Only if we understand and care about the cause of BP's Macondo blowout will we know why it should not have happened and why it should never happen again.*

The data I found were compelling, but I knew it would mean little to those friends and family who still wanted to know "what happened to that rig in the Gulf?" To answer their question, I let the hard data define a chronologically accurate skeletal framework, which allowed me to write a book—*The Simple Truth: BP's Macondo Blowout.*

A key element of my writing goal was to include and use all the data I'd gathered and to explain the technical cause of the disaster for readers across the entire oil and gas arena. But I wanted to do it in a way that, for example, my non-engineering father might have appreciated.

For that reason, and because eleven key personnel from the rig perished that dreadful night and could not speak for themselves, I wrote the book as narrative nonfiction. The data are real, but the story is written as a novel with made-up characters—surrogates for those who survived and those who died.

More than a hundred literary agents turned down my query letters and manuscript submissions for *The Simple Truth.* Many didn't respond, perhaps because they didn't like my writing. Others turned me down using reasons like "untold litigious liability." It seems they wanted nothing to do with the risk of an unknown author telling *The Simple Truth* about a major disaster.

So, I self-published *The Simple Truth* in September 2012. I worked with Amazon to publish paperback and ebook versions.

To date, sales are nice, comments are positive, and I'm in the black. But it's also important for me to look back to when an industry leader read my book and called me in late 2012. As an executive for a major energy company, he invited me to attend a corporate HES (health, environment, and safety) conference to present the results of my research findings. And so began my third career as a professional speaker about Macondo.

As referenced in my acknowledgements, I made seventy-five presentations about BP's Macondo blowout across the U.S. and international to energy companies, professional societies, technical conferences, petroleum engineering universities, civic groups and environmentalists. After my last presentation in Brisbane, Australia, I declared an end to my seventy-three-month, passion-driven, self-imposed Macondo mission.

Yet it hasn't been a clean break because at virtually every technical presentation somebody asked for a copy of my slides. I always apologized before I turned them down—because I had an obligation to make my slides available to SPE so that SPE could publish the slides on their website. I have fulfilled that obligation, so SPE members can now go to the SPE-DL site and see the slides.

But—those slides contain none of the text included herein. Accordingly, this document—*From the Podium: BP's Macondo Blowout*—is the only complete, annotated, footnoted resource about my research-related presentations and recommendations.

Presentation Format

This presentation—*From the Podium: BP's Macondo Blowout*—includes my slides, text, and Q&A from four years of presentations, including my 2015-16 SPE-DL road trip.

Audience members who scheduled an hour and who participated in extensive Q&A got very close to hearing the full story, as told here. Audiences scheduled to listen for only forty-five minutes got less. Some Q&A sessions garnered a question or two; others lasted an hour or two. Significant Q&A topics are included herein.

Though this written text is comprehensive, there are a number of topics in *The Simple Truth* that could not be covered in *From the Podium*. In general, if a topic was not *germane* to understanding the physical *cause* of the blowout, I've left it for *The Simple Truth* to tell the more-comprehensive, fully footnoted, story. However, I have included a few of the 160-plus footnotes and references from *The Simple Truth*, each of which may help readers to better understand the *cause* of the blowout.

This document, especially when paired with *The Simple Truth*, is intended for the general reading public, but it is particularly important to petroleum engineering faculty and students and to all others in the O&G industry (including members of SPE) who care about and want to understand the *cause* of BP's 2010 Macondo blowout in the Gulf of Mexico.

Nevertheless, and for the record, the following is not an SPE presentation, nor is it presented here as an SPE document.

Accordingly, whether you are a layman or a technical expert, if you care about the *cause* of the blowout, I hereby invite you into my world.

Speaker Introduction

John Turley worked as a young engineer for Phillips Petroleum Company and Tenneco Oil and Gas, and then taught petroleum engineering at Marietta College in the US before joining Marathon Oil Company, where he served as Gulf Coast drilling manager, UK operations manager, manager of worldwide drilling, and vice president engineering & technology. He holds a professional degree in petroleum engineering from Colorado School of Mines, an M.S. degree in ocean engineering from the University of Miami, and an executive management degree from Harvard.

After he retired, John independently researched the 2010 Macondo blowout and published *The Simple Truth*—a facts-based book in which he examines the engineering *cause* of BP's Macondo blowout aboard the Transocean *Deepwater Horizon*. He has spoken on the topic to numerous technical, academic, and industry audiences around the world.

It is my pleasure to introduce John Turley.

FROM THE PODIUM:

The Cause of
BP's Macondo Blowout

The Presentation

After such an introduction, I shake hands with the host, go to the podium, and pick up the mic.

I use no notes.

A title slide is already on the screen.

My presentation follows.

FROM THE PODIUM—GOAL

- *Assess* petroleum-engineering, operations, and drilling data from BP's 2010 Macondo blowout in order to define and understand the *cause* of the disaster, and
- *Apply* lessons learned to future wells

SLIDE 1

Assessing and *applying* are key words in my presentation.

Our goal will be to trace and understand the failure mechanisms that led to and *caused* the Macondo blowout[1], so that we can apply what we learn to future wells. We're going to do this by looking at data, all data, from a petroleum engineering perspective.

Let's begin by looking at the Macondo well prior to the blowout.

---

[1] BLOWOUT—Formation fluids flowing up a well into the environment without control. Blowout, by definition, means lack of well control; hence, the emphasis on kick-control (well-control) training. Industry wide, highly experienced rig crews (toolpushers, drillers, company men) react immediately to resolve every well-control event. When such actions fail, for whatever reason whether human or mechanical, the result can be a blowout.

MACONDO—THE PLAN

- **Drill an Exploration Well in the Gulf of Mexico (Mississippi Canyon Block 252)**
- **Spud October 2009**
- **Depth: Approximately 20,000 ft (6,100 m)**
- **Water: Approximately 5,000 ft (1,525 m)**
- **Target: Geological structure (called Macondo)**
- **Target Depth: Below 17,000 ft (5,200 m)**

SLIDE 2

In late 2009, BP (the operator) began drilling its 20,000-foot exploration well in a mile (about 5,000 feet) of water, utilizing an anchored rig named Marianas. That rig was ultimately damaged by a hurricane and replaced by the *Deepwater Horizon* in 2010.

The target was a deep geologic structure (nicknamed *Macondo*) below about 17,000 feet subsea. The nickname allowed for private discussions in public places, without identifying the well. But it also meant the well became the *Macondo* well, and the ultimate disaster became the *Macondo* blowout.

So—let's jump deep into the well, to about 17,000 feet.

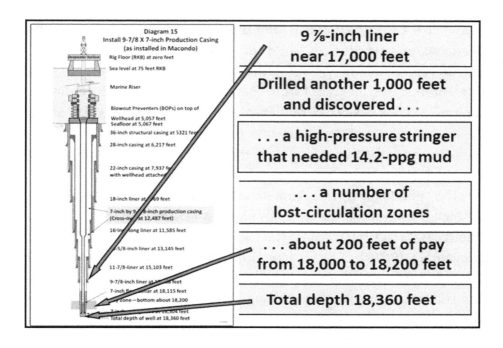

SLIDE 4

Note: The tiny words in the *diagram* (on the left, above, noted as diagram 15,) are extracted from *The Simple Truth* and are not specifically important to the presentation. But—the big words on the right side do matter. Readers are invited to review details of all diagrams as extracted from *The Simple Truth* at the end of this work (including a full-size copy of diagram 15, herein, on page 109).

# # #

Slide 4 shows the floating rig (*Deepwater Horizon*) and the Macondo well. The rig, using GPS and thrusters to stay on location, was considered a *vessel underway*; hence, it had a captain and was regulated by the US Coast Guard (USCG). And that's why the USCG (rather than the federal MMS)[2] led the original post-blowout depositions of survivors and personnel related to the Macondo well and the blowout.

A note of interest: Since the *Deepwater Horizon*[3] was a powered vessel, like a ship, its name in print is always in italics. Conversely, the Marianas, an anchored rig, is not considered a powered vessel at sea; therefore, its name is not italicized. Though not part of this presentation, see diagram 1 from *The Simple Truth*, page 95 herein, for a photo of the Transocean Marianas, and diagram 7, page 101 herein, for an early photo of the *Deepwater Horizon*.

Now, back to **slide 4** (and, yes, there is no slide 3, as replaced by two lines of text in slide 4).

The floating rig was connected to the Macondo well by a 21-inch-diameter marine riser, also known as a drilling riser (capacity about 1500 barrels). The riser was connected to the blowout preventers (BOPs), which were firmly connected to the wellhead (casing head), and in turn to the structural casing strings that penetrate the seafloor. All subsequent drilling activities took place through the drilling riser.

The 18 ¾-inch, 15,000-psi BOP stack, solidly fixed to the wellhead, was topped by two 10,000-psi annular BOPs (though one was de-rated to 5,000 psi to accommodate stripping 6⅝-inch drillpipe). Below the annular BOPs were three VBRs (variable-bore rams), a blind-shear ram (BSR), and a casing shear ram. The lower VBR was dedicated to act as a test ram. (See diagram 5 from *The Simple Truth*, BOP schematic, Page 99 herein.)

As drilling progressed, using synthetic-oil-based mud, multiple strings of casing were run to just below 17,000 feet (see **slide 4**, the upper big arrow). After drilling out and testing the 9⅞-inch shoe to 16.0 ppg (pounds per gallon), the operator then took a few days to drill the next thousand feet of wellbore, with several interesting findings.

Early on, a ten-foot-thick stringer of sand required 14.2-ppg mud. The operator would have liked the drill-ahead mud weight to be heavier, but persistent lost-circulation zones below the sand stringer proved to be sensitive to increased mud weights and required massive doses of lost-circulation material (LCM)[4] to control mud losses.

And then good news: The operator drilled a 200-foot-thick oil-and-gas discovery "pay zone" (see **slide 4**, the lower arrow). The pressure of fluids in the pay zone proved to be 1,000 psi underbalanced (less than) than the pressure exerted by the 14.2-ppg mud column[5].

With the 10-foot sand stringer under control, the lost circulation zones plugged, and the pay zone over pressured by 1,000 psi, the operator drilled an additional 160 feet of wellbore below the pay zone to look for additional hydrocarbons, and to ensure adequate footage of wellbore below the pay zone for well-logging and casing operations.

---

[2] MMS—MINERALS MANAGEMENT SERVICE—The regulatory authority for offshore operations in federal waters. By October 2010, the MMS was reorganized and renamed the BOEMRE (Bureau of Ocean Energy Management, Regulation, and Enforcement), which was then replaced by the BSEE (Bureau of Safety and Environmental Enforcement) and the BOEM (Bureau of Ocean Energy management). Which means the MMS is no longer extant.

[3] The Transocean *Deepwater Horizon* was built in 2000. The dynamically positioned (DP) semisubmersible was also referred to as a MODU—Mobile Offshore drilling Unit. It was rated for 10,000 feet of water and a well-depth of 30,000 feet. The rig measured 396 feet by 256 feet with a 242-foot-tall derrick. Because rig was DP while hovering over a fixed location on the seafloor (the well), the Coast Guard considered it a "vessel underway," which is required to have a Master (captain). Additionally, because the facilities were massive, with accommodations for 130 personnel, federal regulations called for an Offshore Installation Manager (OIM). An on-duty toolpusher was in charge of all drilling facilities and rig personnel associated with drilling the well. The company man worked for BP, and was responsible for managing the well—engineering, logistics, data, decisions, services, costs, and executing procedures.

[4] LCM—Lost circulation materials. Anything designed to plug leaking, fractured, mud-swallowing formations. Shredded cotton and ground-up walnut hulls have been replaced over the years with sophisticated lab-manufactured plugging agents. A slug or "pill" of the material, pumped down to drillpipe and into the annulus, is quite often successful. Or not.

[5] MUD WEIGHT EQUATION: $P = MW \times D \times 0.052$. Here, P is pressure, in pounds per square inch (psi), MW is mud weight, in ppg (pounds per gallon), and D is depth in feet below the top of the mud column (important to use true vertical depth). The constant—0.052—keeps the units straight for feet, ppg, and psi.

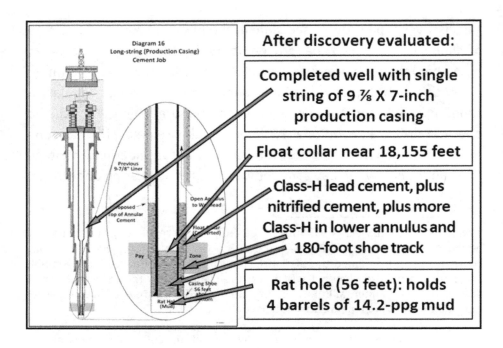

After discovery evaluated:

Completed well with single string of 9 ⅞ X 7-inch production casing

Float collar near 18,155 feet

Class-H lead cement, plus nitrified cement, plus more Class-H in lower annulus and 180-foot shoe track

Rat hole (56 feet): holds 4 barrels of 14.2-ppg mud

SLIDE 5

After extensive well-logging and formation-testing activities, the operator made a bit trip to bottom and then ran a single string of 9⅞-inch X 7-inch production casing[6] (see top arrow in **slide 5**). The operator used a 5,000-foot-long drillpipe[7] workstring to get the top of casing down to the wellhead, where the casing was hung with a casing hanger. (For a scaled-up version of diagram 16 from *The Simple Truth*, see page 110.)

The casing was landed 56 feet above the bottom, and for good reason. Specifically, in deep-water operations, the casing hanger, located on top of the casing, must reach and seat inside the casing head, at the seafloor, *before* the bottom of the casing reaches the bottom of the well. The opposite would be disastrous—requiring the too-long casing string to be pulled from the well and sent back to town for the threaded connections to be redressed.

The 56 feet of open wellbore below the casing (see lowermost arrow in **slide 5**) was called the rat hole, an area of importance to the rest of this discussion.

A twin-flapper float collar (see the second big arrow) had been installed in the Macondo production casing string, near the middle of the pay zone. The flappers in the float collar were designed to act as one-way check valves. If and when they were closed, flow *up the casing* would not have been possible.

Note: See the schematic of the float collar, diagram 14 from *The Simple Truth*, page 108 herein.

But there was a catch. The casing was run (as designed) with the flappers blocked open, so that, as the casing was lowered into the wellbore, mud[8] filled the casing from the bottom up. Then, as planned, the open flappers were "converted" into high-pressure check valves. Conversion was initiated (as typical) by increasing the fluid flow through the float collar (while circulating bottoms up or while displacing the cement) to a predetermined rate (barrels of mud per minute). The *converted* flappers then became one-way check valves.

Two kinds of cement[9] were used for the production casing (see the third big arrow, **slide 5**, pointing to the gray stuff inside and outside the casing). The lead slurry (uppermost in the annulus) was 16.7-ppg Class H cement, which was followed by lightweight nitrified cement (generally across the pay zone), and finally by additional 16.7-ppg Class H cement as the tail slurry. The Class-H tail slurry filled the lowermost annulus and filled the inside of the bottom 180 feet of casing, called the shoe track (see the third big arrow). The shoe track is the interval of casing between the float collar and the guide shoe (bottom end of the casing). The combined heavy and lightweight slurries in the annulus were designed to ensure the cement column did not exceed 14.2 ppg, because of the lost-circulation zones.

So—with casing and cement in the well to protect and isolate the pay zone, the next operation was temporary abandonment.

# # #

Why *temporary abandonment*?

Producing hydrocarbons from a deep offshore well is radically different than producing from shallow-water and onshore wells, either of which can produce oil and gas in weeks or months after drilling is complete.

Conversely, in deep water, the general plan would include drilling one or more delineation wells[10] to better define reservoir geometry and the size of its reserves. Then a subsea development team, using the acquired data, would design the seafloor production facilities, pipelines, and receiving stations necessary to accommodate production of crude oil and natural gas. And then all that equipment would become the focus of a major construction and installation project. Hence, from the time a deep-water exploration discovery[11] is made, years go by until the field first produces hydrocarbons, called *first oil*.

Hence, the then current need for *temporary abandonment* of the Macondo well.

---

[6] CASING STRING—the entire length, comprised of many joints of casing (each about 40 feet long) screwed together. As the well gets deeper, additional casing strings will be run and cemented in place. Each successive casing string must be smaller diameter than the already-installed casing string. The final casing for Macondo (9⅞-inch X 7-inch) was run as a single continuous section.

[7] DRILLPIPE—(or drill pipe)—a joint of drillpipe is a single length of steel tubing (normally 5-, 5 ½-, or 6⅝-inch diameter), usually 30 feet long. Drillpipe has larger diameter couplings (tool joints) for strength and wear resistance.

[8] DRILLING FLUID (Mud)— The simplest drilling fluid is water, but it doesn't carry cuttings very well unless its viscosity is increased. Mud density (measured in pounds per gallon—ppg) provides fluid pressure, or hydrostatic head. Water-based muds use water, clay for viscosity, and barite for density, as minimum ingredients. Synthetic-oil-based muds (SOBM) are environmentally superior muds synthesized from vegetable oils, sugar alcohols, or sugar glucose. In complex geology and deep wells, SOBM is often necessary to make the hole "slicker" to help keep the drill bit from getting stuck.

[9] CEMENT—All casing strings placed in drilled holes need cement to keep them in place and to isolate rocks, fluids, and pressures. Cement slurry is pumped down the inside of the casing and up the outside (the annulus). By adding chemical retarders, the cement slurry is kept pumpable (called green cement, with the consistency of a chocolate malt) for a pre-determined number of hours, to allow time for pumping and for resolving problems.

[10] DELINEATION WELL—After a successful discovery well, the operator's next well(s) in the area would be drilled to help delineate and quantify the discovery zone (the geometry of the accumulation and amount of oil and gas). These answers are needed before the operator can proceed with the design and economics of a development plan; hence, the normal three years or more from discovery, through delineation, through development wells, and the installation of development facilities, before first oil.

[11] DISCOVERY—A discovery is a well that contains commercial quantities of recoverable oil and gas. If not, it is a dry hole.

> **AFTER THE CASING AND CEMENT JOB,
> TEMPORARY ABANDONMENT WOULD INCLUDE:**
>
> ① **Prepare well for testing and the rig for abandonment**
>
> ② **Positive and negative pressure tests—prove wellbore secure or remediate as necessary**
>
> ③ **Install Lockdown Seal Ring (LDSR)**
>
> ④ **Set and test cement plug**
>
> ⑤ **Displace riser with seawater**
>
> ⑥ **Pull BOPs and Riser**
>
> ⑦ **Release the Rig**

SLIDE 6

That means, as noted in **slide 6**, the cased-and-cemented Macondo well was ready to be tested and secured (temporarily abandoned), so the rig could be released—an event scheduled for *the next day*—and sent to its next contracted location.

① The next location for the *Deepwater Horizon* was to have been a previously drilled well that required water-based mud. But Macondo was using a synthetic-oil-based mud. Therefore, a planned activity for *preparing the rig for temporary abandonment* included displacing all the mud from the drilling riser, and then sending all the recovered mud, plus several thousand additional barrels from the mud pits, to a workboat for onshore disposal. That exercise also included getting rid of several hundred barrels of leftover, 16-ppg, water-base, lost-circulation materials (LCM). Getting rid of the mud and LCM was done simultaneous to other Macondo temporary-abandonment operations.

② Two important pressure tests were designed to ensure, prior to releasing the rig, that there was no leak in the wellbore. First, a 2,700-psi *positive-pressure test* (from the BOPs down to the top of the float collar, near 18,000 feet) successfully proved there was no leak from inside the casing to outside the casing. Then, a *negative-pressure test* successfully showed that, with reduced pressure inside the wellbore, there was no leak from outside the casing to inside the casing.

③ The lockdown seal ring (LDSR) is designed in conjunction with the casing hanger and casing head. The LDSR[12], when attached to a 5,000-foot-long drillpipe workstring and lowered through the drilling riser to the casing hanger, would lock and seal the casing hanger in place, forever preventing uplift and leaks. For a schematic of the LDSR, see diagram 17, from *The Simple Truth*, page 111 herein.

④ Even though the well was cased with steel pipe and surrounded by annular cement, with another 180 feet in cement in the shoe track, and given that the float collar contained two one-way high-pressure check valves, *that was still not enough security*. So—the well plan called for one last cement plug in the casing, below the seafloor. This plug would typically be 300 feet long, and would be allowed to set-up and harden, after which it would be tested with a drill bit to ensure its structural and pressure integrity.

⑤ With the well thus declared to be secure, it was then planned to displace the drilling riser with seawater and capture and recover its contents—about 1,500 barrels of oil-based mud—which could not be dumped into the sea.

⑥⑦ Given that the well was pressure tested and declared secure, and the riser's mud was displaced with seawater, the last steps were to be strictly mechanical—pull the riser and BOPs, and then release the rig.

UNFORTUNATELY—DURING THE PROCESS OF DISPLACING THE RISER WITH SEAWATER, THE WELL BLEW OUT.

SLIDE 7

What? How can this be? The operator seemingly followed the above steps, ran good casing, got a good cement job, obtained good pressure tests inside and out, and left high-integrity flow barriers in the wellbore.

But the fact is, as shown in **slide 7**, the well did blowout while the drilling riser was being displaced with seawater. The unexpected violent eruption of oil and gas from the riser, through the rig floor, and up inside the derrick, *seemingly* came from nowhere, without warning. Explosions and fire followed. Eleven men died. The rig burned and sank. The months-long oil spill that followed was an environmental disaster.

Bottom line—a fundamentally sound temporary-abandonment procedure turned into a tragically lethal catastrophe. And that should not have happened. Therefore, something had to be wrong with the above list, and every step must be examined.

But first—given that the near-term post-blowout world was fraught with litigious, political, personal, corporate, and unbounded media hype seemingly with no end in sight, a few ground rules were established. Like—ignore finger pointing, he-said-she-said, politics, litigators, deep pockets, companies, and pontificating experts. Further, establish a non-committee, no-deadline, no-vested-interest solo focus to *assess rig data* to define the *cause* of the Macondo blowout.

Therefore, starting at the top of the list (**slides 6 and 7**) and working down the page, it's time to look at rig data and other hard evidence that may or may not have been critical to the entire operation.

A good starting point, because it was critical to *Prepare the well for testing and the rig for abandonment*, is data that define the casing and cement job.

---

[12] CASING-HANGER LOCKDOWN SEAL RING (LDSR) has two primary purposes: (1) it accepts the sealing mechanism for a future subsea production tree, and (2) with the LDSR in place on top of a casing hanger, the casing hanger cannot be lifted from its metal-to-metal seals. Until the LDSR locks the wellhead in place, the annular seal (casing hanger inside wellhead) is dependent entirely on the weight of the casing. Without the LDSR, the casing hanger can be lifted by a strong upward pull or pushed upward by differential pressure (when the pressure above is less than the pressure below).

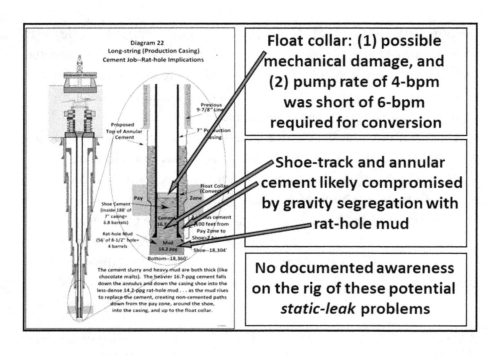

SLIDE 8

Recall that the float collar (the top big arrow in **slide 8**) needed to be "converted" to have its flappers function as dual high-pressure check valves. The manufacturer had performed (pre-blowout) laboratory tests using Macondo's 14.2-ppg oil-based mud and determined that a 6-bpm (barrel-per-minute) minimum pump rate was required to produce the pressure drop inside the float collar necessary for conversion. (Note: For a schematic of float-collar conversion see diagram 22, from *The Simple Truth,* on page 113)

Yet records show that after the casing was installed, the pump rate into the casing, while circulating mud and displacing cement, never went above 4.1 bpm. That means the float collar was never converted, and the open flappers never acted as high-pressure check valves. And the path up the wellbore was wide-open.

There was also contention (during court testimony) that residual rock cuttings may have entered the casing (as often happens) while the casing was being lowered into the open-hole section of the deep wellbore. Such cutting may have settled and plugged the guide shoe and/or float collar, which then required more than 3,000 psi to break circulation (to dislodge the cuttings).

Further arguments claimed that such high pressure may have even breached (made a hole in) the casing just below the float collar. These points form the basis for a later discussion (**Q&A #2**), but the data confirm this: the well ultimately flowed *upward* through the float collar, so the flappers had to have been open, and therefore had not been converted.

The data pertaining to cement in the shoe track (below the float collar) are also important. Think of oil and vinegar, where separation is common, given that the less-dense fluid (oil) floats on top of the heavier fluid (vinegar). The same thing happens in wells with rat holes, especially if the mud in the rat hole is less dense than the cement slurry above it (in other words, the slurry in the shoe track and the annulus). For Macondo, the 14.2-ppg mud in the rat hole was significantly less dense than the 16.7-ppg Class-H cement slurry in the lower annulus and inside the 180-foot-long shoe track.

This is not a surprise phenomenon—American Petroleum Institute (API) RP (Recommended Practice) 67 Section 7.5[13] specifically identifies and addresses the problem and recommends that a heavy "pill" of mud (a few barrels) be placed in the rat hole prior to running the casing, so that gravity segregation will not occur. This was not done on Macondo. (This topic is covered in **Q&A #3**, to follow.)

Such predictable gravity segregation in the Macondo well allowed lighter-weight (14.2-ppg) oil-based mud to percolate upward from the rat hole into the 16.7-ppg cement in the bottom of the annulus, where it was only one hundred feet to the bottom of the pay zone. Further, the same percolation phenomena allowed mud from the rat hole to simultaneously migrate upward into the casing and contaminate the 180 feet of 16.7-ppg shoe-track cement.

Bad news: There were two potential sources of a static leak path between the annulus and the wellbore: (1) the unconverted (open) float collar, and (2) the oil-based-mud-contaminated cement in the lower annulus and inside the casing shoe track. A third potential leak path was through breached casing (to be discussed in **Q&A #2**).

Good news: The potential leaks were *static* because the wellbore was still full of 14.2-ppg mud, which yielded a hydrostatic pressure that was 1,000-psi overbalanced compared to the pressure of the reservoir. This was also good news because the next steps in the abandonment procedure called for *testing for leaks* and repairing as necessary.

# # #

So, it was time two pressure tests—a positive-pressure test and a negative-pressure test.

The 2,700-psi positive-pressure test was accomplished by closing the fully functional (important later) blind-shear rams (BSR)[14] and using the cement-unit pumps to raise the pressure below the BSR and down into the wellbore. Such pressure extended from under the BSR down to the top cement wiper plug, which was on top of the float collar. The cement plug had a solid-core, so the increased wellbore pressure above the plug could not get past (below) the float collar. The pressure was held for thirty-minutes. (Note: See diagram 5, page 99, for a schematic of the Macondo BOPs, taken from *The Simple Truth*.)

The test was done in two steps—low pressure first, then the higher-pressure thirty-minute test. All data indicate the positive-pressure test successfully proved there was no leak from the inside the casing to the outside of the casing (between the BSR and the top cement plug, located on top of the float collar).

So, it was time to get ready for the negative-pressure test (NPT)—not to be confused with the same acronym (NPT) when used for non-productive time.

---

[13] RAT HOLE—Rat hole is any section of open wellbore (previously drilled hole) left below casing. The O&G industry long ago realized the implications of leaving rat hole under (below) newly installed casing. The industry collectively adopted

an RP—a Recommended Practice—to handle a common problem. As per API RP 65 Section 7.5—"If casing is not run to bottom, the *rat hole* should be filled with a higher weight mud to prevent cement from falling into the rat hole and displacing rat hole mud into the cement column . . . "

[14] BLIND SHEAR RAMS—The BSR's two steel blades face each other. When actuated, they close, cut, and seal the wellbore. Rated for 15,000 psi. They will cut drillpipe but will not cut through a tool joint or heavy casing. To ensure the blind shear ram will work when needed, the driller keeps track of the depth of critical tool joints (in the area of the BOPs). If necessary, for example during a kick, the driller will raise or lower the drill string to get tool joints away from the blind shear rams.

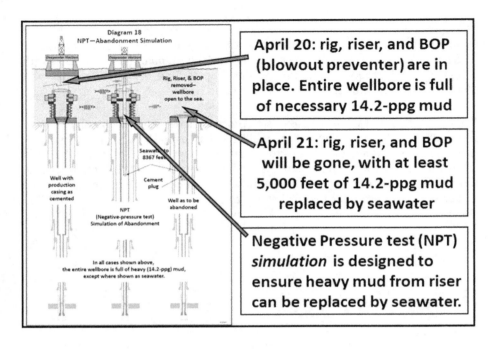

April 20: rig, riser, and BOP (blowout preventer) are in place. Entire wellbore is full of necessary 14.2-ppg mud

April 21: rig, riser, and BOP will be gone, with at least 5,000 feet of 14.2-ppg mud replaced by seawater

Negative Pressure test (NPT) *simulation* **is designed to ensure heavy mud from riser can be replaced by seawater.**

SLIDE 9

Look at **slide 9**, the far-left schematic shown in diagram 18. The 18,000-foot wellbore was full of 14.2-ppg mud. The well was dead—1000-psi overbalanced. Nothing was leaking (despite the *potential* static leaks).

(Diagram 18 from *The Simple Truth* is on page 112.)

Given the passage of time, the schematic on the far *right* of diagram 18 depicts the Macondo well as early as "tomorrow." There was to be no BOP, no riser, and no rig—and the well would have lost at least 5,000 feet of 14.2-ppg mud (from the riser) and replaced it with 5,000 feet of 8.6-ppg seawater. With such radical changes, there was a need to know (before pulling the BOP and riser) if the associated loss of hydrostatic pressure (almost 1,500 psi, from the BOP down to the float collar) would cause a leak and allow external fluids to enter the wellbore.

Alternatively, disconnecting and lifting the BOPs to look for leaks would not have been a good idea.

Better yet, the operator would *simulate* the loss of hydrostatic head with a *negative pressure test* (NPT)[15] by making the wellbore think the top 5,000 feet of mud had been replaced by seawater.

Important—even before taking the first step, there were two possible results from the successfully implemented negative-pressure test (NPT):

(1) **Good news**: If during the NPT simulation (with pressures throughout the wellbore significantly reduced) the wellbore showed no leak for thirty minutes—then the casing (having already passed the high-pressure test) would be deemed pressure secure, and the temporary-abandonment process could proceed; or

(2) **Also good news**: If the NPT simulation revealed there was an active leak anywhere from the annulus (outside the casing) into the reduced-pressure wellbore, then the temporary-abandonment process would be delayed, and the required repair job (likely with cement) would commence immediately. It would have been *good news*, not because there was a leak, but because *identifying and remediating* any such leak was mandatory—and it was exactly the reason for the negative-pressure test.

So, the next step was the negative-pressure test—the NPT.

----

[15] NEGATIVE-PRESSURE TEST (NPT)—For deep-water wells being temporarily abandoned, it is necessary to pull the BOPs when the well is done. But this means all the mud in the riser (above the seafloor), which had been necessary to control the well, will be replaced by seawater. To ensure the casing is mechanically secure before the BOPs are pulled and the heavy mud is lost, an NPT is designed to simulate the replacement of riser mud with seawater. If a casing leak is detected via the NPT, the fix is mandatory and may call for repairing and securing the wellhead or drilling out and perforating and squeezing cement into the area of the leak (at a casing connection or at the casing shoe).

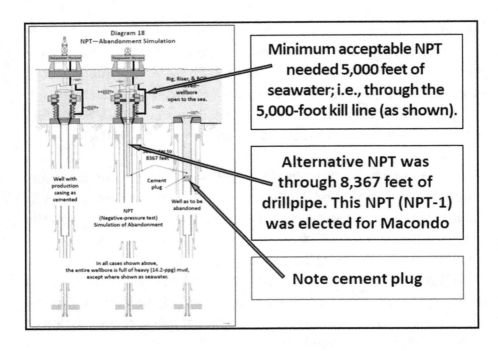

SLIDE 10

The drilling riser had a number of external, built-in, high-pressure lines, one of which was the kill line. For clarity, the kill line was added to diagram 18 (page 112), as per the upper big arrow.

The 3¹/₁₆-inch-diameter, 15,000-psi kill line reached from the rig floor to the BOP—about 5,000 feet. By filling the kill line with seawater and then closing the BOP (above the kill-line opening), the 18,000-foot-deep wellbore saw 5,000 feet of seawater on top of 13,000 feet of heavy mud. This mixed-fluid column *simulated* what the wellbore (from the sea floor down to the float collar) would see if the BOPs were lifted in the 5,000-foot-deep Gulf. Such a test (an NPT using a 5,000-foot-long kill line) would have met the approved regulatory requirements for testing the Macondo well.

However, data indicate the operator elected to run an even-more-rigorous NPT, using 8,367 feet of drillpipe (second big arrow in **slide 10**) rather than 5,000 feet of kill line. The middle pictorial in diagram 18, above, shows the drillpipe hanging through the BOP, down to 8,367 feet.

The stated purpose of the deeper NPT was to accommodate the installation of the LDSR (lockdown seal ring). The LDSR (which locks and seals on top of the casing hanger inside the casing head) had to be either pushed down, or pulled down, with 100,000 pounds of load. The operator elected to use about 3,000 feet of heavyweight drillpipe below the wellhead to *pull down* on the LDSR, which required 3000 feet of room below the casing head.

The final cement plug (bottom arrow in diagram 18 above) was therefore planned to be installed and tested below that depth (near 8,300 feet) to provide the necessary clearance for the LDSR installation.

All that planning meant the negative pressure test (NPT) would utilize the 8,367-foot-long drillpipe workstring (and not the 5,000-foot kill line).

For convenience, we call the 8,367-foot negative-pressure test *NPT-1*.

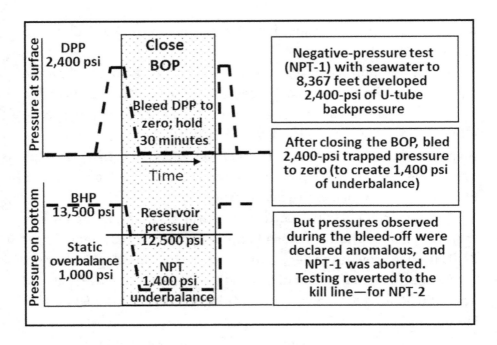

SLIDE 11

Slide 11 is a graphic pictorial of NPT-1 pressures (using 8,367 feet of drillpipe).

The upper half of the graph (dashed line) generalizes the pressure-gauge readings at the top of the drillpipe (the gauge was located at the cement unit), and the lower half of the graph (dashed line) generalizes simultaneous pressures at the top of the float collar (with a *hypothetical* pressure gauge located at the float collar).

In the lower graph, note that the bottom-hole pressure (BHP), with a full wellbore of 14.2-ppg mud, is about 13,500 psi. Also, note that the main reservoir pressure (the pay zone) is about 12,500 psi (the difference was the 1,000 psi of overbalance mentioned earlier).

In the upper graph, the observed drillpipe pressure increased from zero (0 psi) to 2,400 psi as the 8,367-foot workstring was filled with seawater. This trapped pressure was "backpressure"—a measure of the u-tube effect of the 14.2-ppg mud column outside the drillpipe and the 8.6-ppg seawater on the inside.

Note that the bottom-hole pressure (BHP) at the float collar (lower graph) did not change as the drillpipe was filled with seawater.

But then the fully functioning (important later) annular BOP was closed around the drillpipe. The closure isolated 5,000 feet of heavy mud in the drilling riser (outside the drillpipe) from the rest of the wellbore. The closure also created a single, closed, fluid-filled system comprised of 2,400 psi at the rig floor (on the top of the drillpipe), above 8,367 feet of seawater (inside the drillpipe), on top of the remaining column of 14.2-ppg mud (about 10,000 feet from the bottom of the drillpipe to the float collar). This single fluid column (plus the 2,400-psi on the drillpipe) continued to exert a bottom-hole pressure (BHP) of about 13,500 psi at the float collar. Note that the pressure at the float collar did not change when the BOP was closed.

Given that the wellbore was a closed and fluid-filled system, if there was a 100-psi decrease in the 2,400 psi of trapped pressure (on the drillpipe), every pressure in the wellbore would have dropped by 100 psi (decreasing pressure is shown on both graphs). This proactive reduction was accomplished by opening a valve at the cement unit and allowing a small volume of seawater to escape the drillpipe (like releasing air from a balloon). Then the exercise was repeated, and each reduction of trapped pressure on top of the drillpipe had a corresponding reduction of pressure inside the drillpipe and throughout the wellbore below the closed BOP.

When the operator back-flowed additional increments of seawater and dropped the trapped pressure by a total of 1,000 psi, the pressure inside the wellbore at the top of the float collar was then equal to the reservoir pressure (though the wellbore and the pay zone were separated by casing, cement, and the float collar). This was noteworthy, because at that time the pay zone was neither overbalanced nor underbalanced compared to the wellbore pressure inside the casing.

The operator then continued dropping the drillpipe pressure by back-flowing additional small volumes of seawater, step-by-step (barrels out, pressure down), until the goal of zero (0 psi) was reached (a total pressure reduction of 2,400 psi). At zero (0 psi) on the cement-unit surface gage, the wellbore pressure (BHP) at the float collar was 1,400-psi *underbalanced* compared to the pay zone (located outside the casing).

The regulatory requirement for Macondo's NPT called for dropping the pressure to zero (0 psi) and observing it for thirty minutes. The goal was to determine if the reduced pressure stayed at zero (0 psi), which would indicate no leak, or if the shut-in pressure increased above zero (0 psi), which would indicate a leak.

But there was a problem during the test.

Once the trapped backpressure on the drillpipe was dropped from 2,400 psi to about 200 psi, it would not decrease further. Even after opening the cement-unit valve and allowing as much as 15 barrels of seawater to flow from the drillpipe to the cement unit, the drillpipe pressure would not go to and stay at zero (0 psi).

Because the drillpipe pressure would not bleed to zero (0 psi) even when the drillpipe was opened, and because 15 barrels of seawater had flowed back to the cement unit during the five-minute period ending at 6:00 P.M., the valve at the cement unit was closed (at 6:00 p.m.) and not reopened.

These phenomena were declared (on the rig, and in USCG depositions) to be the result of "the bladder effect." For more on this topic (see **Q&A #1**).

NPT-1 was therefore considered *anomalous* (flawed) and the test was *aborted*.

The Macondo negative-pressure-test procedure was therefore switched from the 8,367-foot drillpipe test (*NPT-1*), to the 5,000-foot kill-line test (deemed *NPT-2)*.

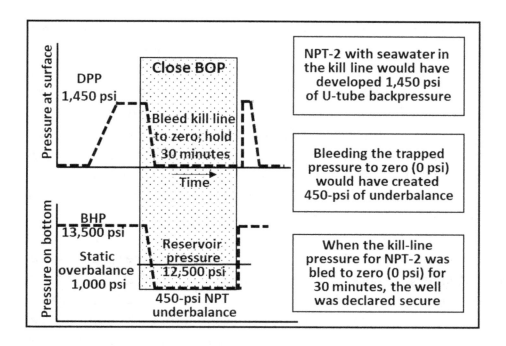

SLIDE 12

If NPT-2 had been run using the NPT-1 procedure, then **slide 12** (top of diagram) would have represented the kill-line pressure at the rig floor. And the bottom half of the diagram would have shown the pressure at the float collar for NPT-2, using the 5,000-foot kill line.

The 5,000-foot kill line, when filled with seawater, would have exhibited 1,450-psi of trapped u-tube pressure (5,000 feet of 14.2-ppg mud in the riser acting on the bottom of the kill line, which contained 5,000 feet of seawater).

Then, with the BOP closed, bleeding the 1,450 psi to zero (0-psi) would have generated 450 psi of underbalance. This test, when completed, would have met regulatory requirements, whether it showed no leak (casing integrity with no flow from the outside the casing), or it showed an increase in pressure, which would have indicated a leak that needed to be repaired.

Good news: The kill-line pressure was successfully dropped to zero (0 psi), where it held steady for the required thirty minutes. That meant the well could be, and was, deemed secure, ready for the rest of the temporary-abandonment procedure, including displacing the riser with seawater to recover the heavy mud for onshore disposal.

Bad news: The well was known to *not* be secure (because it later blew out). Therefore, something had to be wrong with one or both of the negative-pressure-test procedures, results, and/or conclusions.

That translates to a mandatory need to go back and look deeper at all aspects of NPT-1 and NPT-2.

To do this, actual mudlogging pressure charts, as recorded offshore, in real time, must be assessed. These charts were, fortunately, generated on the rig and sent wirelessly to onshore computers[16]. After the blowout, the operator made the charts available to the courts and to the public through its own internal investigative reports (referenced on the next page, headline at the top of **slide 13**).

---

[16] BP and its operating partners (in offices) had access to the real-time (offshore) data through *Insite Anywhere*, BP's electronic data system owned by Halliburton. The system provides (and records) real-time flow-in and flow-out data, gas analysis data, pressures, and other drilling data.

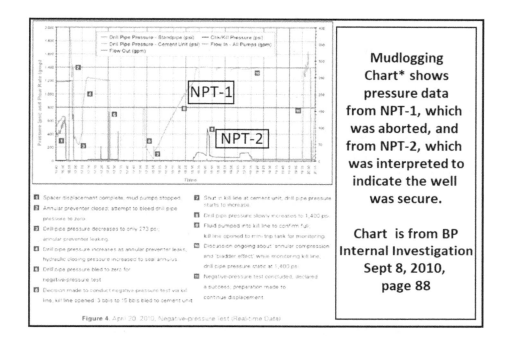

Figure 4. April 20, 2010, Negative-pressure Test (Real-time Data)

Mudlogging Chart* shows pressure data from NPT-1, which was aborted, and from NPT-2, which was interpreted to indicate the well was secure.

Chart is from BP Internal Investigation Sept 8, 2010, page 88

SLIDE 13

The time/pressure mud-logging chart (**slide 13**) shows measured surface pressures (vertical axis) for NPT-1 drillpipe pressures and subsequent, simultaneous NPT-2 kill-line pressures. Each horizontal pressure line is 200 psi, and the time labels are five minutes apart.

(A full-scale version of the mudlogging chart is on page 114.)[17]

For NPT-1, a key area of interest is the short diagonal line between 5:55 and 6:00 P.M. This is the recording of that last 200 psi that would not bleed off for NPT-1. More on this later.

But the data to the left (prior to 5:55 P.M.) is also of interest because it appears to have set the stage for an important decision yet to be made. In short, when the annular BOP was first closed around the drillpipe for NPT-1, and the pressure *under* the annular BOP was severely reduced (as per the NPT procedure), heavy fluid from the riser leaked *down* past the rubber sealing element (the bladder) of the annular BOP and pushed seawater back up the drillpipe. And yes, the fluid level in the riser had dropped accordingly.

No big deal—standard operating procedure—the driller increased the closing pressure on the annular BOP. Then it happened again. Same leak, same result.

When the annular-BOP closing-pressure was ultimately increased enough to withstand the 2,400-psi pressure *reduction* (under the BOP) required for NPT-1, no additional fluid leaked past the BOP (and the riser stayed full). More on this later in a discussion about "the bladder effect" (and in **Q&A #1**).

Now, back to the short diagonal line at 5:55 P.M. In the next slide, the same data are shown on an increased scale.

––––––––––––––––––––

[17] This chart is from BP's *Deepwater Horizon* Accident Investigation Report. The internal investigation was released to the public on September 8, 2010. Section 2.6 interpreted the negative-pressure test. This chart, referenced as Figure 4— April 20, 2010, Negative-Pressure Test (Real-time Data), appeared in the report on page 88.

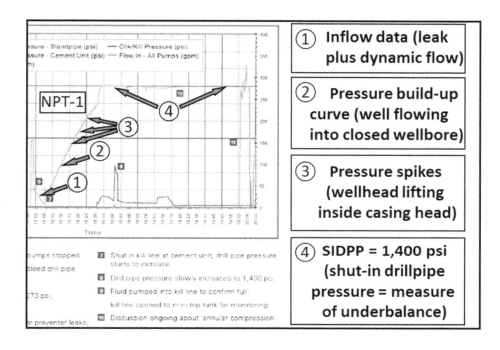

①	**Inflow data (leak plus dynamic flow)**
②	**Pressure build-up curve (well flowing into closed wellbore)**
③	**Pressure spikes (wellhead lifting inside casing head)**
④	**SIDPP = 1,400 psi (shut-in drillpipe pressure = measure of underbalance)**

SLIDE 14

The boxed #1 arrow in **slide 14** points to a short diagonal line from 5:55–6:00 P.M. That line is the drillpipe pressure recording when Macondo first began to flow at 5:55 P.M. During that five-minute period, with the drillpipe open, the well *flowed* 15 barrels of seawater from the drillpipe to the cement unit, and the pressure refused to go to zero (0 psi).

That was not supposed to happen.

The 15 barrels of unidentified fluid (the source) that displaced 15 barrels of seawater had to have come from somewhere. Two choices— from the riser or from the wellbore. But the fluid level in the full riser was static. Fifteen barrels in five minutes is 4,000 barrels a day. The data say the well—the pay zone—was flowing at 4,000 BPD.

The reality that the reservoir was flowing is based on data from the rig, as follows.

At 6:00 P.M., the short-duration *vertical* line indicated the valve at the cement unit was closed (no more flow to the cement unit).

But the flowing reservoir (not yet affected by the 6:00 P.M. closure of a valve 3-1/2 miles away) continued to flow into the under-pressured *closed* wellbore, which increased the wellbore pressure, as if blowing up a balloon. The ever-increasing wellbore pressure (recorded at the top of the drillpipe) produced a typical *pressure-buildup curve* (box #2).

Such pressure-buildup curves, with Macondo NPT-1 an excellent example, are often produced and analyzed during the testing of a well (for example, during a drill stem test, or DST) to quantify the flow characteristics of a producing reservoir.

As flow continued into the closed Macondo wellbore and the wellbore pressure increased, the drawdown on the reservoir and the flow rate from the reservoir decreased. Finally, when the reservoir had fully pressured-up the wellbore and flow had stopped (at 6:35 P.M.), the built-up pressure at the surface was 1,400 psi. (See arrows coming from box #4.) That constant, stable pressure was a measure of the original underbalance between the fluid column in the wellbore and the discovery pay zone.

For clarity, consider a common drilling example. If an operator took a kick (formation fluids entered the wellbore), closed the BOP, and observed 1,400-psi on the drillpipe, the pressure would be noted as the SIDPP (shut-in drillpipe pressure)[18]. The SIDPP would be a measure of how underbalanced the wellbore was at the time of the kick.

Likewise, the 1,400-psi stabilized pressure observed during NPT-1 was the SIDPP for the in-progress Macondo kick. The 8,367 feet of seawater on top of 10,000 feet of heavy mud was 1,400 psi underbalanced compared to the 12,500-psi pay zone, which was in open communication with the wellbore; hence, the well flowed—kicked.

The NPT-1 pressure-buildup data provided irrefutable evidence that the source of flow was the 200-foot-thick discovery pay zone.

#

Further, reference is made to several pressure spikes on the pressure-buildup curve (See arrows from box #3). The data (spikes) indicate that something in the pressured system was moving—like a valve opening and closing. Here, the "something" was the casing hanger, where the radical reduction of pressure (2,400 psi) *under* the closed annular BOP and *above* the casing hanger unseated (uplifted) the casing hanger in short bursts, as if belching. Each "belch" was recorded as a spike on the pressure-buildup curve.

Importantly, this unseating of the casing hanger was hard data that meant the LDSR (lockdown seal ring) had not yet been installed. This situation did not contribute to the blowout yet to come, but it did play a role in delaying the kill procedure after the blowout.

# # #

The hard data portrayed in **slide 14** showed solid evidence of annular communication, of flow, and of the well kicking.

Yet, as stated earlier, there was (heated) discussion on the rig (shortly after 6:00 P.M.) that the data generated by NPT-1 (in **slide 14**) proved the test to be "*anomalous.*"

The argument, in part, was that "the bladder effect" (leaking annular BOP bladder) caused the flowback (u-tube) of 15 barrels up the drillpipe, which led to NPT-1 being aborted.

To complicate matters, there were serious world-class petroleum engineers who pontificated on an unrelated form of the "bladder effect" associated with rising gas bubbles, gas trapped under the annular preventer, temperature-expansion criteria, etc. But that level of engineering sophistication was likely beyond the scope of the same-name "bladder-effect argument" on Macondo.

Instead, the term was used loosely on the rig referring to the hours prior to 5:55 P.M. (refer to **slide 13**) when the closing pressure on the annular was insufficient, more than once, and mud from the riser leaked past the annular bladder and expelled seawater from the drillpipe. In these instances, as mud from the riser leaked past the BOP the fluid level in the riser dropped. But when 15 barrels of seawater were expelled from the drillpipe from 5:55 to 6:00 P.M., the fluid level in the riser did not fall.

Three criteria dispel the leaking-BOP argument: (1) the riser remained full of mud, (2) the pressure-buildup curve was a measure of the rate of flow from the reservoir, and (3) the 1,400-psi SIDPP could have been generated *only* be the reservoir, which was 1,400 psi underbalanced to the wellbore.

More on the "bladder effect" in **Q&A #1**.

Nevertheless, based on the argument, a key outcome prevailed— NPT-1 was aborted and NPT-2 was commenced using the kill line.

---

[18] SHUT-IN DRILLPIPE PRESSURE—When a kick is detected and the BOPs are activated (which shuts-in the well), drillpipe and casing pressures are measured and recorded. The shut-in drillpipe pressure (SIDPP) is key to characterizing the kicking formation, wherein the bottom-hole pressure of the kicking formation is the simple sum of the SIDPP and the pressure exerted by the drilling mud (and other fluids as appropriate) in the drillpipe at the true-vertical depth (TVD) of the kick. The shut-in casing pressure (SICP) can be high and erratic, due to the unknown volume and type of formation fluids (oil, water, and especially gas) moving up the wellbore.

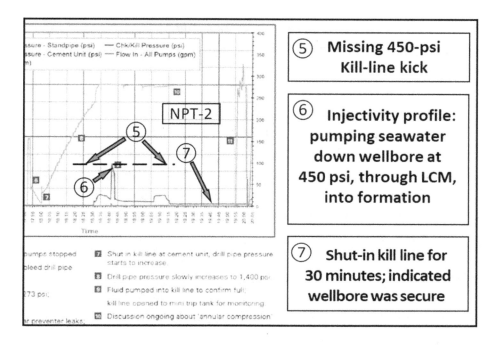

SLIDE 15

NPT-2 utilized the kill line, which was full of seawater. As noted in **slide 15** (with the valid NPT-1 data still recording in real time), the NPT-2 data showed two anomalies, though neither (apparently) got enough attention to shut down the test.

The **first** anomaly—NPT-2 was missing the 450-psi kick (arrows from box #5), which was the kill-line equivalent of the 1,400-psi NPT-1 kick up the drillpipe.

So, the question was this: How could a very real kick through the wide-open 8,367 feet of drillpipe not manifest as a kick through the wide-open 5,000 feet of kill line? Maybe a kill-line valve was closed.

Whether or not there was a closed valve, something did block the kill line, preventing the kick from being seen at the surface.

So—back to **slide 6**, which provided the steps to be taken for temporary abandonment. Recall the need to get rid of the oil-based mud as well as several hundred barrels of water-based lost-circulation material (LCM). Records show the viscous slug of LCM[19] was pumped *down* the drillpipe and *up* into the lower riser (above the BOPs), where it would act as a spacer between the heavy mud—to be eventually displaced from the riser—and the seawater that would do the lifting.

But there was a problem.

Recall that prior to 5:55 P.M., there were a couple of occasions (at the start of NPT-1) when the closing pressure on the annular BOP was inadequate and mud bypassed the annular BOP and displaced seawater from the drillpipe. The closing-pressure problem was ultimately fixed, but the occasions of heavy mud from the riser dropping and bypassing the leaking annular meant the LCM moved *deeper* into the riser and ended up *in the BOPs* rather than *above the BOPs*.

By design, LCM plugs holes in rocks. But it will also plug holes like the small inside diameter of the $3\frac{1}{16}$-inch, 15,000-psi kill line, the bottom end of which was in the BOP, nested in the slug of LCM. With the bottom end of the kill line plugged by LCM, the 450-psi "push" of the kick apparently could not manifest at the surface.

Or, as previously noted, perhaps the bottom kill-line valve was closed.

This leads us to the **second** NPT-2 anomaly, which occurred when seawater was pumped into the top end of the kill line (and into the wellbore) to ensure the kill line was full of seawater. That would have been a small-volume test, as the fluid-filled, closed wellbore had passed the 2,700-psi positive pressure test (down to the top cement wiper plug on top of the float collar).

Nevertheless, during the act of pumping seawater into the kill line (see arrow from box #6), the pressure increased rapidly (as expected), but (unexpectedly) broke back—rapidly decreased on its own—at about 500 psi *before* the pump was turned off. The break-back pressure-drop appeared equivalent to the break-back pressure-drop one might see during a cement squeeze job. So, even though the kill line should not have been able to take whole fluid, it did.

And that meant the valve at the bottom of the kill line was indeed open. Further, it meant the fluid from the kill line had found an outlet and was being pumped (lost) "somewhere"—like outside the kill line, down the wellbore, and back into the kicking (albeit shut-in) pay zone.

But that begs two questions:

(1) What happened to the LCM that blocked the kill-line kick?

(2) How can fluid be pumped into the formation given the successful results of the 2,700-psi positive pressure test?

First, the 450-psi driving pressure of the kick likely was not enough to pump LCM *up the kill line*, but 500 psi from the top was able to push LCM *away from the kill line* and transmit pressure into the wellbore.

Second, had the top cement wiper plug remained in place on top of the float collar, it would not have been possible to pump past it, into the formation. But the top plug did not remain in place, as it had been lifted away from (above) the float collar by the 15 barrels of pay-zone flow during NPT-1. This meant that when the kill-line pressure exceeded about 450 psi and transmitted its pressure to the wellbore, the pressurized fluid (now overbalanced) found an exit point—back into the formation—turning the Macondo well into an injection well.

The data confirm that with the missing 450-psi kill-line kick, and with "injection-well" communication into the annulus, and with there still being a 1,400-psi kick in progress on the drillpipe—*the entirety of NPT-2 was invalid.*

Nevertheless, with the (unobserved) help of the LCM plug, the kill line showed zero (0 psi) pressure at the surface, and when opened at 7:16 P.M. *discharged no seawater* (see **slide 15**), for more than the requisite thirty minutes; hence, the test was declared to have successfully shown no leak into the casing.

In other words, *NPT-2 was declared **valid** and the well was declared **secure***.

And that meant it was time to get on with the temporary abandonment procedure. Recall in **slide 6** that the remaining steps to be taken included the following: ③ install the LDSR, ④ set a cement plug in the casing, ⑤ displace the riser with seawater, ⑥ pull the BOPs and riser, and ⑦ release the rig.

Data indicate step ⑤ began next, without steps ③ and ④.

This meant the displacement of the riser took place before the LDSR had been set (recall the spikes on the pressure-buildup curve, **slide 14**, arrows from box #3). It also meant the 8,300-foot-deep cement plug (see **slide 9**, middle of right-hand schematic) had not been set, which was designed to further isolate the deep wellbore from the seafloor and the rig.

Instead, the next activity (after declaring NPT-2 successful) included two key steps: opening the BOPs and displacing the riser with seawater.

Opening the (annular) BOP immediately killed the well, since all the heavy mud in the riser once again became an integral part of the 18,000-foot column of heavy wellbore fluid. In fact, the kicking pay zone, even though still open to the wellbore, was immediately 1,000-psi overbalanced by the total mud column.

The Macondo well was dead.

The simple act of opening the BOP, which killed the well, was the upside of the negative-pressure test *simulating* the replacement of the upper wellbore with seawater.

But that good news was short lived.

---

[19] LCM AS SPACER—The operator had asked the contracted mud service company to make up at least two different batches, or "pills," of lost circulation material—one commercially known as Form-A-Set and the other known as Form-A-Squeeze. These (leftover) materials were combined for use as a spacer during displacement of the riser. The combined material weighed 16 ppg. A total of 424 barrels of 16-ppg spacer was pumped into the well and displaced with seawater, placing the spacer 12 feet above the BOP. The operator chose to use the (combined) LCM pills as a spacer so as to avoid having to dispose of the unused material (onshore) as hazardous waste—because the ultimately recovered water-based LCM (then a *used* product) was disposable at sea.

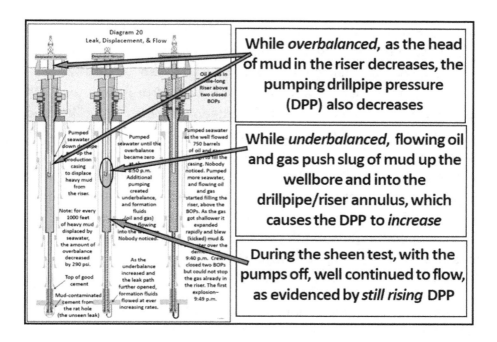

Diagram 20
Leak, Displacement, & Flow

While *overbalanced*, as the head of mud in the riser decreases, the pumping drillpipe pressure (DPP) also decreases

While *underbalanced*, flowing oil and gas push slug of mud up the wellbore and into the drillpipe/riser annulus, which causes the DPP to *increase*

During the sheen test, with the pumps off, well continued to flow, as evidenced by *still rising* DPP

SLIDE 16

At that time, rig leaders were oblivious to the open path from the formation to the wellbore, and they start pumping seawater into the drillpipe (left-hand schematic, **slide 16**). Seawater that exited the bottom of the drillpipe displaced heavy mud from the riser (the drillpipe annulus). As mud was displaced from the top of the riser and replaced by seawater in the bottom of the riser, the circulating pressure (u-tube) on the drillpipe decreased with the reduced footage of annular mud; hence, the drillpipe pressure dropped by the minute.

(A full-sized diagram 20, from *The Simple Truth*, is on page 116.)

With the replacement of heavy mud in the riser by seawater, the total hydrostatic head at the bottom of the well was also decreasing. In fact, with each barrel of seawater pumped, and with each barrel of heavy mud discharged from the riser, and with each minute that passed, the total hydrostatic overbalance on the reservoir decreased from 1,000 psi—until it got to zero (0 psi)—neither overbalanced nor underbalanced. And the operator was still pumping seawater.

And with that next barrel pumped (creating underbalance), that's when the well commenced to flow (middle schematic, **slide 16**).

As the formation flowed, a column of hydrocarbons (oil with natural gas in solution) moved up the deep wellbore, lifting the mud above it. The uplifted mud rose up the casing and around the outside of the drillpipe, which *increased* the backpressure (u-tube) on the drillpipe. Data show the drillpipe pressure stopped falling and started rising—the demarcation between overbalanced and underbalanced—when flow from the reservoir commenced, at about 8:55 P.M.

The operator (apparently) did not see this change in drillpipe pressure and kept pumping seawater.

# # #

Seawater was pumped until the slug of LCM in the riser reached the top of the riser (just under the rig floor). When the rig crew saw the LCM, they turned off the seawater pumps. The LCM was water-based, and since all the oil-base mud in the riser was *above* the LCM, there should have been no more oil-based mud in the riser. A "sheen test" was then initiated to ensure there was no more oil-based mud. Test results showed a positive result (no sheen). Accordingly, rig leaders directed the crew to allow future returns from the riser (including the LCM) to go overboard (since there was no more oil-base mud).

But the rig data said there was a problem.

During the sheen test, while the seawater pumps were off, the well (according to NPT-2) should have been dead. Instead, additional mudlogging charts showed that the drillpipe pressure continued to rise while the pumps were off—*because the well was still flowing*.

Nevertheless, with a good NPT-2 and a good sheen test (and not noticing the well was flowing), the operator went back to pumping seawater, which further exacerbated the rate of flow.

The wellbore schematic on the far right of **slide 16** deserves its own slide.

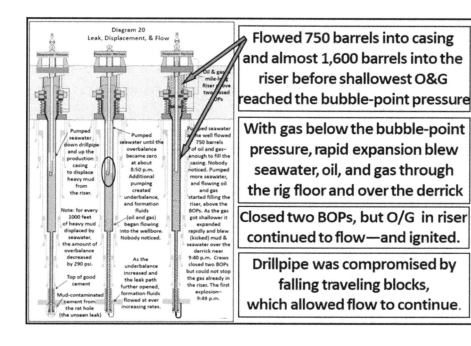

Diagram 20
Leak, Displacement, & Flow

Flowed 750 barrels into casing and almost 1,600 barrels into the riser before shallowest O&G reached the bubble-point pressure

With gas below the bubble-point pressure, rapid expansion blew seawater, oil, and gas through the rig floor and over the derrick

Closed two BOPs, but O/G in riser continued to flow—and ignited.

Drillpipe was compromised by falling traveling blocks, which allowed flow to continue.

SLIDE 17

The well continued to flow (kick) hydrocarbons (right-hand schematic, **slide 17**), until the flow filled the entire 750-barrel wellbore, then filled the BOPs, and then started filling the 1,500-barrel riser. For reference, a 100-barrel kick would be considered *significant*.

Note: The BOPs were still open, and the operator was still pumping seawater.

Somewhere along that rapidly accelerating path up the wellbore and riser (where there was less and less heavy mud to generate hydrostatic pressure, the shallowest gas—normally under enough pressure to remain in solution (dissolved in the oil)—reached the *bubble point*. That meant the dissolved gas finally experienced a pressure so low (due to less hydrostatic head) that it boiled from the oil and formed free gas, in the form of tiny bubbles[20].

And as any given bubble flowed (and was pumped) to an even

shallower depth (lower pressure), the bubble expanded. Perhaps slowly at first, then explosively fast. The collective mass expansion of bubbles displaced the shallowest fluids from the riser and thus further reduced the pressure on top of the already expanding gas. Once started, the process was autocatalytic (the evolved and expanding gas reduced the pressure, causing further expansion and allowing even more gas to evolve from the oil).

Though analog evidence was abundant, the first unquestionable evidence the well was flowing took the form of an eruption of fluids from the riser, through the rig floor, and over the derrick.

Records show "somebody" immediately closed an annular BOP and a variable bore ram (VBR)[21]—(see closed BOPs as shown in **slide 17**).

And herein lies the major difference between deep-water wells and all others, whether offshore or onshore.

When the deep-water Macondo annular BOP was again closed (recall it had been used throughout both NPTs), it worked exactly as designed and expected. It sealed the annulus outside the drillpipe. It stopped the reservoir from flowing (other than pressuring up the wellbore—creating another pressure-buildup curve—below the BOP).

But because the BOPs were on the seafloor a mile below the rig, all the crude oil and natural gas already in the 1,500-barrel riser continued to accelerate up the riser driven by the sub-bubble-point gas, which continued to expand violently.

The exiting oil and gas (from above the closed BOPs) engulfed the rig floor and derrick and blew laterally under the rig floor throughout the moon pool[22] area.

In seconds, engine-room suction fans inhaled a mix of gas and atomized oil, which fueled the diesel engines that drove the power generators. The generator room exploded (data showed 9:49 P.M.), which shut down power throughout the rig. Perhaps ten seconds later, the oil and gas under the rig floor exploded, taking out the moon-pool walls and entering the hallways, quarters, and galley. The entire rig, from substructure to the top of the derrick was engulfed in flames.

Good news: As bad as that was, the well was dead—no new flow could enter the deep wellbore or the riser past the closed BOPs (annular and VBR), or enter the drillpipe, which was mechanically closed (still tied to the seawater pumps).

Bad news: But that changed when the conflagration on the rig floor (fed by burning oil and gas from the riser) eventually brought down the traveling blocks, which would have landed directly on top of, and thus opened, the top of the drillpipe.

Data from a September 2010 DNV (Det Norske Veritas) inspection of the recovered BOP indicated several broken sections of drillpipe landed on top of the closed BOP. The broken (open-ended) drillpipe thus provided a large conduit *through* the closed BOPs, and instantly allowed new formation fluids to enter the highly underbalanced wellbore and riser, further feeding the inferno on the rig.

Some experts argue that the blocks didn't fall, and that the powerless rig drifted off station, which parted the drillpipe (locked high in the blocks and low in the BOPs). The argument is academic without further data, but in any case, the then failed drillpipe became the open conduit right up through the closed BOPs.

---

[20] BUBBLES—BOYLE'S LAW ($P \times V = C$)—No calculating necessary, but the simple equation shows there is a relationship between the volume (V) of a fixed mass of gas, and its pressure (P), in that their product is constant (C). In short, this means that as the pressure on a gas bubble decreases, its volume increases, and vice versa. A common example involves Mentos mints and Diet Coke, where the mixture erupts immediately after the first bubbles form.

[21] VARIABLE BORE RAM (VBR)—Rated to 15,000 psi. The two VBR rams have semi-circular faces that self-adjust around whatever size pipe they find. The enclosed drillpipe is not cut. Closing pressure does not need to be adjusted, as it does for annular BOPs.

[22] MOON POOL—Large opening through the lower deck—directly under the rig floor and surrounded by handrails—through which the BOP and other tools are lowered into and recovered from the sea.

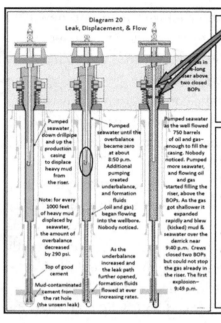

Diagram 20
Leak, Displacement, & Flow

Drillpipe was uplifted by the violent flow. Excess buckled DP was trapped between the closed BOPs, which prevented the blind shear rams from closing.

THE MACONDO BLOWOUT
- Immediate explosions and fire
- 11 deaths
- 115 survivors evacuated the rig, many with extreme injuries
- Rig sank day and a half later
- Almost 5 million barrels of oil flowed into the Gulf of Mexico for 86 days before well killed

SLIDE 18

The two closed BOPs (**slide 18**), in concert with the violent uplift of the flowing well, created a problem with unusual mechanical consequences, which significantly impacted the kill of the well. Specifically, though successfully used earlier for the positive pressure test, the blind shear ram (BSR)—located between the closed lower annular and the closed upper VBR (with open drillpipe between them)—would not close, and could not be forced to close, for weeks and months to follow. And the well continued to flow through the open drillpipe.

In short, when the BOP was recovered from the seafloor in September 2010 and subjected to a forensic examination by Det Norske Veritas (DNV), more drillpipe was found between the two closed BOPs than the distance between them. The drillpipe in the gap was deformed (buckled) and off-center, which had prevented the BSR from closing. Arguments persist among academics and experts as to whether the violent fluid uplift drove excess pipe into the gap or if pressure differentials (inside and outside the drillpipe) between the closed BOPs buckled the pipe.

Given the debate, the bottom line is this: The BSR would not close, and the entrapped drillpipe was subsequently found to be severely buckled. The deformed, distorted pipe was so far off center the blades of the BSR could not function.

Also, the drillpipe inside the closed annular BOP was found to be externally fluid eroded, an indication of the violence of the flow even as the annular BOP was first closing.

A second serious impact of the BSR-buckled-drillpipe problem was that the emergency riser disconnect system depended on the BSR closing. That meant the auto-disconnect system at the LMRP (lower-marine-riser package) would not release. The LMRP included a remote-operated connector between the two annular BOPs, which, when released, would have disconnected the LMRP and the riser from the rest of the BOP stack. Therefore, the rig was stuck on location, unable to release from the riser or BOP stack.

The long-term environmental and financial consequences of the blowout are well documented, but key statistics define the tragedy.

Eleven men died. Survivors totaled 115, though more than half sustained serious and crippling physical injuries.

The *Deepwater Horizon* burned and sank a day and a half later. See the photo, diagram 21 from *The Simple Truth* , on page 117 herein.

The Macondo well flowed ("about" is a safe word) five million barrels of crude oil into the Gulf, before being killed on day 86. Events and procedures during those terrible 86 days are beyond the scope of this work, which remains focused on the *cause* of the tragedy.

So—where do we go from here?

SLIDE 19

With all the above helping us to understand the sequence of events that *caused* the Macondo blowout, let's look *back* at what we've seen as well as *forward* to how we can apply what we've learned to future activities.

Slide 19 lists factors that *contributed* to the blowout. Alone, any might seem innocuous. Yet, for Macondo, none was. And had any one of them been recognized and acted on with authority, the tragedy likely would have been averted.

(1) The footage of the *rat hole* was necessary as part of the procedure for evaluating the discovery and landing the long string of production casing. Yet industry experts realized decades ago that less-dense rat-hole mud could gravity segregate *upward* into heavier cement slurries in the casing and in the annulus (see **Q&A #3** for additional information). Such upward migration of mud would contaminate the cement. Mud-contaminated cement does not set,

does not harden, and does not seal as designed. Preventing this known problem would have been easy—with zero rig time and zero risk—during the original design of the well.

Nevertheless, the design program for the well stated, "*Do not need to set 16.5 ppg mud in rat hole as volume is only ~4 bbls.*"

That directive *contributed to the cause of the blowout.*

#

(2) The *float collar* played a role that could have been so different. By design, the float collar contains two high-pressure flappers that act as one-way check valves (preventing flow up the wellbore). The flappers are run in the open position so the casing fills with mud as it is being run. By design, the float collar must be "converted" for the flappers to activate as check valves. (See diagram 17 from *The Simple Truth*, page 111, herein.) The manufacturer tested the model programmed for the Macondo well, using Macondo mud, and confirmed the float collar would convert at a minimum throughput pump rate of 6 bpm. Data from the rig show the maximum pump rate at the float collar was 4.1 bpm. Therefore, the float collar did not convert, and the flappers never got the chance to act as check valves.

The open float collar *contributed to the cause of the blowout.*

#

(3) *Back-flowing the well* contributed on several fronts. Specifically, during the last 200-psi of the 2,400-psi NPT-1 drawdown, the contaminated cement in the lower annulus and the 180-foot shoe track finally yielded to the increasing *negative* differential pressure, and the well commenced flowing. That initial surge further cleared the mud-contaminated annulus-to-wellbore path, and the well rapidly flowed 15 barrels into the low-pressure wellbore during the next five minutes (5:55 to 6:00 P.M.).

The flow also lifted (back flowed) the top cement plug from the float collar, which subsequently allowed seawater injection into the kill line during NPT-2 (pushed the plug back toward the float collar).

Further, the continued flow of formation fluids into the

underbalanced wellbore created the pressure-buildup curve (indicative of the reservoir's flow capacity). The buildup-curve pressures increased for thirty-five minutes and leveled-off at 1,400 psi, a measure of the underbalance between the flowing reservoir's formation pressure and the NPT-1 mixed fluid column (8,367 feet of seawater on top of 14.2-ppg mud).

The lack of recognition that the well was flowing during NPT-1 *contributed to the cause of the blowout*.

Records also reveal a significant in-court debate that centered on the possibility of a pre-NPT-1 breach in the casing below the float collar. This topic is to be covered in **Q&A #2**.

(4) *Unseen forensic data* is a big category. It includes all the flow-related data evidenced by the pressure chart for NPT-1 as well as other documented mud-logging flow-and-pressure charts. All these data were unseen, or more fairly, were neither seen nor understood to an extent sufficient to lead to a firm decision to stop testing and remediate whatever problem had allowed flow from the reservoir into the cemented production casing.

Further, NPT-2 provided two additional key pieces of unseen forensic data. First, there should have been a simple two-part drawing showing the following: (a) the NPT-1 wellbore, with its specific seawater-filled drillpipe and mud column, and its shut-in pressure (kick pressure) of 1,400 psi, side by side with (b) the NPT-2 wellbore, with its specific seawater-filled kill line and mud column, and its shut-in pressure (kick pressure) of—

Whoops, a simple calculation says—the NPT-2 drawing should have shown a 450-psi shut-in pressure (kick pressure) on the kill line.

It's the *missing* part that would have been so vivid in a simple drawing of the wellbore with balanced hydrostatic pressures up the drillpipe and up the kill line. Neither seeing nor missing the 450-psi kill-line kick pressure contributed to a falsely justified comfort with NPT-2.

By the same token, the data that showed the kill line to be full of seawater also showed that "something gave" when the kill line was pressured up. That data, apparently unseen, showed injection into the reservoir (in other words, communication with the annulus). Missing the assessment of "what gave" contributed to the comfort level in declaring NPT-2 a good, no-leak test.

The lack of assessment and response to the above noted forensic evidence *contributed to the cause of the blowout.*

#

(5) LCM in the BOP did not cause the blowout, but it plugged the kill line and allowed the NPT-2 test pressure to be dropped to zero (0 psi), which made NPT-2 look good—and that *contributed to the cause of the blowout.*

#

(6) *Simultaneous operations* (pumping mud overboard to a workboat, moving mud and cleaning mud pits, and preparing for the next day's operations) also *contributed* by making it difficult to accurately measure pit levels[23] *and mandatorily balance* barrels of seawater being pumped into the well with the barrels of mud, LCM, and seawater exiting the riser. To the extent possible with such incomplete data, post-blowout analysis and cross-correlation of charted data (beyond the simplicity of pit-volume totalizers and differential barrel counters with alarms) showed the well to be flowing (more barrels out of the well than being pumped in) before 8:55 P.M., but these data were either not seen or not acted on to such an extent as to recognize the flow, stop the work, and initiate well-control procedures—all of which *contributed to the cause of the blowout.*

#

Though each of the above *contributed to the cause of the blowout*, several factors were more directly linked to *causing the blowout.*

---

[23] PIT-LEVEL—Critical to drilling and all wellbore-related activities is an active record of the number of barrels of drilling mud in the system—both in the wellbore and in a number of interconnected mixing and storage pits on the rig.

While drilling, the system is dynamic, with mud being pumped into the well and mud returning up the annulus (the riser). At other times the system is static—nothing moving. Whether static or dynamic, sensitive gauges and meters compare pit volumes and pump rates 24/7, with a simple reality—any loss of mud from the system likely means lost circulation, and any gain of mud by the system (called a pit gain) likely means a kick. The driller watches such readings (which are audibly and visibly alarmed), so he or she can take immediate action as necessary. The mudloggers monitor the same charts and alarms around the clock on behalf of the company man and toolpusher and immediately raise the alarm as warranted.

Factors evidenced by data that
Caused and Exacerbated
the blowout

- Viable NPT results that confirmed a leak and the well's flow potential if underbalanced
- The lack of a primary cement-plug barrier before seawater displacement
- Viable pump-pressure data that confirmed the well flowed for an hour prior to the blowout
- Massive, unchecked flow (kick) that ultimately debilitated proper functioning of the BOPs

---

SLIDE 20

The items listed in **slide 20** are strongly linked to the *cause* of the blowout:

(1) NPT-1 data showed that the Macondo wellbore was in communication with the annulus and that the well flowed when exposed to a pressure reduction of about 2,400 psi (underbalanced by 1,400 psi). Such confirmation should have (mandatorily) given the Macondo leaders no viable recourse other than to stop the temporary-abandonment procedure, investigate and identify the location of the leak, and remediate as necessary. Every action on the rig after the well was shut-in at 6:00 P.M. and after the leak/flow data were declared anomalous and further ignored—and every unseen intervention opportunity along the way, including data from NPT-2—drove the operation closer to the cataclysm that would follow.

(2) A critical barrier for any temporarily abandoned wellbore (for

example, when preparing for a hurricane) is the 300-foot-long cement plug normally set a few hundred feet below the seafloor. It is designed with a single purpose in mind—plug the wellbore so *nothing* can get through the plug. Had the cement plug been set *after* NPT-2 (even if that test was wrongly considered valid) and *before* the riser was displaced with seawater, the story would have ended quite differently.

 • Based on data that showed what had and had not been done prior to the blowout, a critical plan-changing decision had (apparently) been made to set the cement plug *after* the riser was displaced, ostensibly so the cement plug would be set in seawater rather than in oil-based mud. As part of the same decision, this would have delayed the setting of the lock-down seal ring (LDSR) but would have allowed it too to have been set in seawater rather than in mud.

On both counts, this meant the riser was displaced with seawater and the well blew out prior to setting the cement plug and the LDSR.

(3) Pump-pressure data gathered while displacing the riser with seawater provided *extensive* incontrovertible evidence the well became balanced (neither overbalanced nor underbalanced) and commenced flowing near 8:55 P.M. Had the evidence been recognized early on, immediate action would have allowed rig crews to shut in the well and kill a *low-volume, low-pressure kick*—prior to remediating the then-obvious casing-cement-leak problem.

(4) The Macondo blowout preventers (BOPs) have taken a lot of heat since the blowout due to this argument: The *blowout preventers* did not prevent the blowout. Point taken, but the topic is an important part of this presentation.

The normal pressure-testing and well-control functions of a BOP are well known (as taught in petroleum-engineering universities, on the job, and through mandatory, professional, well-control schools around the world). Specifically, as related to well-control kicks, the critical goal is to *minimize the volume* of uninvited formation fluids that enters the wellbore. Accordingly, rig leaders and crew are skilled at recognizing *early* symptoms of kicks (flow from the well, gain of drilling fluid in the pits, etc.). After the *very first symptom* of a possible kick, prudent operator and contractor personnel take immediate necessary steps to allow closing the BOP as soon as possible. The immediate closing of the BOP minimizes the severity of the kick by preventing further influx of formation fluids and allows rig crews to gather necessary information to quantify the kick and kill the well.

Not so with Macondo. As shown herein, the steps that contributed to and caused the blowout took place *hours* before the BOPs were called into action. The well first flowed during the induced pressure drop associated with the NPT-1 simulation (yes, that was a 15-barrel *kick*). The well was shut in (with a valve at the cement unit, rather than with a BOP) near 6:00 P.M.

Later, after NPT-1 and NPT-2, with open BOPs and the help of seawater pumps, the well lost its overbalance (about 8:55 P.M.) and kicked and flowed for almost an hour. The flowing well filled the casing and most of the riser with nearly 2,000 barrels of crude oil and natural gas, and then blew out (about 9:45 P.M.) with violent, gas-driven energy through the rig floor and over the crown of the derrick—before the lower annular BOP was closed. A variable-bore ram BOP was also closed.

The first explosion occurred near 9:49 P.M.

As described above (following **slide 18**), the combination of the extremely long-duration kick and accelerating, voluminous flow contributed to lifting and buckling the drillpipe inside the BOP stack, specifically inside the BSR, located in the gap between the lower closed annular BOP and the upper closed VBR.

Note: Although the blind shear ram (BSR) had been used earlier in the day for the 2,700-psi positive-pressure test, the buckled drillpipe prevented the BSR from closing. Had the debilitated BSR been able to close and seal, the duration of the *in-progress* blowout would have been measured in hours and days rather than weeks and months.

SLIDE 21

Worldwide, degree programs most often referred to as *petroleum engineering* and *petroleum technology* are the only academic programs dedicated to teaching the engineering concepts necessary for drilling wells, controlling the complexity of subsurface fluids and pressures, completing wells for production, producing hydrocarbons, and managing the vast underground geologic complexes in which oil and gas are found. After graduation, petroleum engineers (and others, for sure) further mature through on-the-job training, specialized course work, graduate school, and years of experience to ensure a deep understanding of the concepts required for a career in the energy business.

For Macondo, as noted in **slide 21**, the engineering concepts that define the cause and manifestation of the Macondo blowout are not overtly complex. No differential equations. No spreadsheets. No sophisticated software packages. Conversely, with a clear understanding of hydrostatics, mud weights, fluid pressures, cement, casing design, wellbore mechanics, well-control requirements, and formation flow criteria—basic Drilling 101[24]—no petroleum engineer[25] or experienced rig leader reading this document should be overwhelmed by any aspect of the Macondo blowout data.

However, knowing and understanding basic concepts is different from applying such knowledge to managing any and every well—as should have been done on Macondo, without question, without fail.

#

While *From the Podium* focuses only on the *Macondo data* that define the *cause* of the blowout, others—academic and engineering study groups, corporations, consultants, authors, technical experts, journalists, legal entities, and environmental groups—tirelessly investigate and pontificate on topics beyond the cause and effect aspects of the Macondo blowout, including human factors, group think, finger-pointing, company culture, training requirements, politics, metrics analysis, liability assessment, completion procedures, regulations, real-time data, process safety, root and latent cause analysis, operator and service-company relationships, toxic dispersants, product-service-resource initiatives, riser-gas detection, disaster management, non-Macondo historical catastrophes, equipment redesign, drilling reliability, drilling process safety, risk management, and other "could've, would've, should've" topics without limit. Entire books have been written on these topics and more.

Are such studies and related findings good? Oh, yes! They are *umbrella* issues because they pertain to Macondo and the entire industry. Each is a critical issue, being examined by the best of the best, and all for a good cause: to help minimize the chance of ever repeating a Macondo-type disaster.

But the above slide ends with the word *BUT. BUT* what?

---

[24] DRILLING 101—Slang term for the first-semester course in drilling engineering as part of petroleum engineering curriculum. Topics include drilling equipment,

drill bits, rock mechanics, drilling fluids (mud), wellbore hydraulics, casing design, cement, and well control to name a few

[25] ENGINEER—uses math and science to make projects faster, safer, and more productive, cost efficient, and environmentally friendly. Petroleum engineers apply geo-science and engineering (mechanical, structural, civil, geological, electrical) to the petroleum industry, whether designing, drilling, and managing wells, or producing oil and gas (O&G), or managing O&G reservoirs.

```
┌─────────────────────────────────────────────────┐
│                  Conclusions                    │
│                                                 │
│  •  Macondo blowout evidence is defined by basic │
│     petroleum-engineering, operating, and drilling │
│     concepts, training, and responsibilities    │
│  •  Skilled application of such concepts would have │
│     made a difference at Macondo                │
│  •  Also helpful would have been industry initiatives like │
│     drilling process safety, human factors, real-time data, │
│     and safety & environmental management systems, │
│  •  ┌──────────────────────────────────────────┐ │
│     │  But . . . HOW DO WE APPLY LESSONS LEARNED │ │
│     │    FROM MACONDO TO FUTURE WELLS?          │ │
│     └──────────────────────────────────────────┘ │
│                                                 │
└─────────────────────────────────────────────────┘
```

SLIDE 22

Although involved experts strive for closure and applicability of the complex, seemingly open-issue "umbrella" topics, the question must be asked, as in **slide 22**: *How do we apply what we've learned from the Macondo disaster to future wells?*

The mix of senior leaders on Macondo, despite their collective education, experience, and responsibilities, failed to sufficiently action abundant real-time data in a way to prevent the disaster. Such failure is not acceptable. Would different leaders—whether clones of the Macondo team or hand-selected world-class deep-water drilling experts—have had different results? Likely, but we will never know.

Nevertheless, regardless of who was or could have been in charge, the following is offered as a tool that—had it been used on April 20, 2010 to assess and respond to real-time Macondo data—likely would have saved the day.

SLIDE 24

(And, yes, the contents of **slide 23** have been included in **slide 24**.)

NASA and the commercial aviation industry use a proven concept that can be paraphrased as "process interruption" to solve unexpected, intractable, and otherwise lethal events. Certainly, a commercial flight to Dallas takes off, climbs, cruises, navigates, approaches, and lands. For a passenger to be able to say, "That was a good flight," every step in the process must have worked, in the right order, even if there were problems prior to disembarkation.

Sometimes, though, flights are interrupted by process mishaps. Think about Captain Chesley Sullenberger and the incident often called *Miracle on the Hudson*. Or *Apollo 13*, where an oxygen tank failed a mere 200,000 miles from earth. In both cases, the immediate and expert response to the respective process interruptions saved the day.

Now, the challenge—translate the concept from flying a space shuttle or an airplane to drilling a well.

An exploration well (**slide 24**)—from rig mobilization, through sequential drilled intervals, casing and cement jobs, evaluation, and rig demobilization—can be defined as a continuous sequence of processes that must be completed before we can say, "That was a good well." Here, though, a single process might be a *casing job*, followed by a process called *cementing*, followed by a process called *drilling to the next casing point*.

As with flying, every process in the scheduled well must be completed before the next step can be taken, and each step must be completed with success, even if there are problems along the way.

And that means, if any step in any process is interrupted by an unplanned or unexpected result (equivalent to engine failure, or loss of hydraulic power, or stuck landing gear, or an Apollo 13 audible alarm), then something is wrong—and the problem must be fixed.

A drilling example follows.

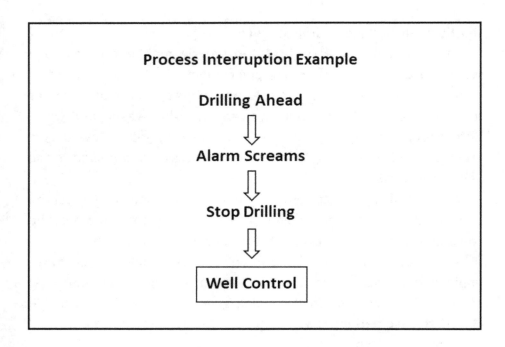

SLIDE 25

Few things are worse than doghouse coffee on an offshore rig.

But a screaming alarm (**slide 25**) on the rig floor can instantly overshadow vile coffee and cause the driller to stop drilling, shut down the mud pumps, pick-up off bottom, and close the annular BOP.

Well control for a full-fledged kick is perhaps akin to a pilot realizing he's just lost power. In both cases, it's time for immediate response and deliberate actions because the penalty for failure can be high. And on a rig, that's exactly what rig leaders and crews are trained to do.

But before going further, there's something wrong with the rig-floor-alarm, stop-drilling, well-control example. Because it's too simple.

And that's because a rig-floor alarm while drilling at 15,000-feet below sea level requires the same in-depth scrutiny as does an alarm in the cockpit while flying at 15,000 feet above sea level.

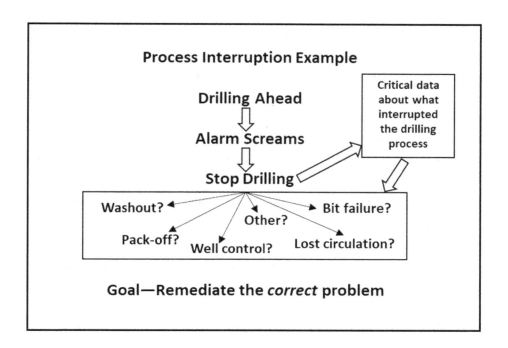

SLIDE 26

The problem is this: Several things, in addition to a kick (**slide 26**), can interrupt the process of drilling. Many are alarmed, but some are not, and even these need rapid response.

For example, an immediate drop in standpipe pressure may indicate a washed-out tool joint, where a few-seconds delay by the driller in picking-up off bottom and shutting-down the mud pumps may be the difference between a bit trip and a fishing job.

Further, a reduction of (or no) mud returns, or a drop in total pit volume, may be lost circulation—just the opposite of a kick.

All drilling parameters on the rig floor and at the bit—torque, drag, pump pressure, rate of penetration, mud weight, gas in returns, weight on bit, pit volume, mud properties, pick-up and slack-off, etc.—are measured and monitored for a reason. A change in a single parameter could mean nothing, or it could be something that demands immediate attention.

Hence, it's critical to all parties (and practiced throughout the industry) that whenever the drilling process is interrupted by an alarm—or by any audible or visual signal, event, or unexplained happening—the first step is to *stop drilling*. Only then can the time be taken to look at critical data and determine the source of the interruption so the problem can be identified and solved.

Hah! No big deal. That's what every rig around the world does while drilling.

But no drilling operation can afford to limit such prudence to just when the bit is on bottom.

For example, the Macondo disaster happened *not while drilling*, but during what should have been a straightforward, end-of-well, temporary-abandonment procedure.

Hence, we need to define a procedure, a protocol, that applies to every process throughout the entire well, during drilling of course, but *not just during drilling*.

And we will call the procedure our **Process Interruption Protocol**.

It's the protocol (the procedure) we will use if any aspect of any process gets interrupted.

> If any process related to the well
> is interrupted
>
> The
> *Process Interruption Protocol*
> must be . . .
>
> - **Stop the process**
>
> - **Resolve the Interruptive data**
>
> - **Remediate the Problem**

SLIDE 27

Here, as shown in **slide 27**, the same procedure that works for the process of drilling (drilling gets interrupted . . . so we (1) stop drilling, (2) resolve the data, and (3) remediate the problem) needs to be applied to every process throughout the well.

If we are running casing (in other words, the process of running casing), and any step in the process gets interrupted (for instance, the casing gets stuck, or mud returns are lost, or the well kicks), then the *Process Interruption Protocol* says:

(1) Stop running the casing.

(2) Assess the data that accompanied the interruption.

(3) Remediate the problem.

Process Interruption Protocol—
Negative Pressure Test

PROCESS
- Run the drillpipe
- Fill with seawater, close the BOPs
- Bleed trapped pressure to zero (0 psi), hold 30 minutes

INTERRUPTION
- Pressure would not bleed; the well made 15 barrels

PROTOCOL
- Stop the Process (NPT 1)
- Resolve the interruptive data (slide 29—1,2,3,4)
- Remediate the problem (fix the leak).

SLIDE 28

What if, as per **slide 28**, the *Process Interruption Protocol* had been applied to the *Macondo negative-pressure test*?

The Macondo NPT process was straightforward.

(1) Run the drillpipe.

(2) Fill it with seawater.

(3) Observe the amount (2,400 psi) of trapped back-pressure.

(4) Close the annular BOP.

(5) Bleed small amounts of seawater from the drillpipe to incrementally reduce the trapped pressure.

(6) Continue bleeding seawater and reducing the trapped back-pressure until it gets to zero (0 psi).

(7) Hold the pressure at zero (0 psi) for 30 minutes, watching for any indication of a leak.

(8) Then, if there is no pressure increase (no leak), declare the well

secure.

(9) Conversely, if the NPT shows there is a leak, fix the problem.

# # #

But something happened (*the interruption*) during the Macondo negative-pressure test (NPT-1)—see items (5) and (6) above. The trapped pressure was manually reduced, as per the procedure, to about 200 psi. Nevertheless, while further manually bleeding seawater from the drillpipe to reduce the pressure from 200 psi to zero (0 psi):

(1) the drillpipe returned about 15 more barrels of seawater than expected, and

(2) the drillpipe pressure would not bleed to zero (0 psi).

Here, because the NPT was interrupted, the **Process Interruption Protocol** says:

(1) Stop the NPT.

(2) Resolve the interruptive data.

(3) Remediate the problem.

# # #

Wow, how clean and neat the problem would have been resolved, in gross contrast to one of the most lethal, costly, man-made, environmental disasters in history.

# # #

So, let's look back at the mud-logging chart that showed NPT-1 data.

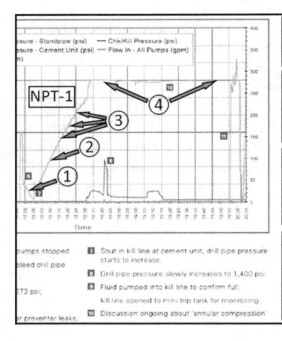

1. Inflow data (leak plus dynamic flow)

2. Pressure build-up curve (well flowing into closed wellbore)

3. Pressure spikes (wellhead lifting inside casing head)

4. SIDPP = 1,400 psi (shut-in drillpipe pressure = measure of underbalance)

SLIDE 29

For the 8,367-foot-deep NPT-1, as shown in **slide 29**, the *interruptive data* presented itself from 5:55–6:00 P.M. (arrow from box #1)

The **Process Interruption Protocol** says that when faced with *interruptive data* that was not part of the plan, *stop the process*, which means *stop NPT-1*. No more negative-pressure testing. No NPT-2. Now is the time to put the entire focus on the NPT-1 *interruptive data*.

A thorough examination of the *interruptive data* at the end of NPT-1 reveals, without ambiguity, that there are only two likely sources of the extra 15 barrels of seawater from the drillpipe:

(1) through a leaking annular BOP, or

(2) from the deep wellbore and annulus.

In looking at the *interruptive data*, we would have asked if the annular BOP closing pressure was again insufficient and if mud from the riser had again bled past the annular and forced 15 barrels of seawater up the drillpipe. For Macondo, the data show otherwise. The riser was checked (after 15 barrels flowed back) and was found to be full of drilling mud. Therefore, no mud leaked from the riser past the annular BOP to lift seawater up the drillpipe.

See more in Q&A on this topic (**Q&A #1**).

As we continue to look at the NPT-1 6:00 P.M. *interruptive data*, the other alternative is that the reduced wellbore pressure—severely underbalanced by NPT-1—somehow invited flow from the annulus into the wellbore. *And since we ran the negative-pressure test to look for leaks—perhaps we've found one.*

This supposition would have matched the data, as such flow down the annulus and up the casing would lift seawater from the drillpipe, and the same flow would disallow us to bleed the drillpipe pressure to zero (0 psi). For these reasons (along with the immediately subsequent pressure-build-up curve and the 1,400-psi shut-in drillpipe pressure), the data show without ambiguity that the flow was from the deep reservoir, down the external-casing annulus, and up into the underbalanced (low-pressure) shoe track and wellbore.

Alternatively, as later argued in court, if the casing had been breached (for example, a hole in the casing just below the float collar), the flow path would have been directly from the pay zone into the side of the casing, rather than down the annulus and up the shoe track. This topic is discussed in **Q&A #2**.

Hence, had the ***Process Interruption Protocol*** been followed for Macondo, NPT-1 would have been officially stopped shortly after 6:00 P.M., and the *interruptive data* (bolstered by the build-up data that immediately followed) would have led to the right assessment. That correct assessment would have been that the *interruptive data* generated by the significantly reduced NPT-1 wellbore pressure did the following:

(1) *proved communication with the annulus* and

(2) *invited the formation to flow into the underbalanced wellbore.*

As a direct result of applying the ***Process Interruption Protocol***, the simple conclusion at the time would have been this:

(1) There is a leak between the wellbore and the annulus.

(2) The problem must be investigated and remediated before continuation of the temporary-abandonment procedure.

In hindsight, and with weeks and months to look at data, it was discovered that float-collar and rat-hole problems caused the silent leak. But on the rig, in real time, those conclusions were not so obvious.

Nevertheless—

This clear-cut, unambiguous, data-based assessment of annular communication would have led the operator to mandatorily change the temporary-abandonment plan, and to commence identification and remediation of the leak, without the risk of a well-control incident.

SLIDE 30

As summarized in **slide 30**, the purpose of this presentation is to show that an engineering *assessment* of Macondo data justifies *application* of a simple, proven, problem-solving methodology (*Process Interruption Protocol*) that not only would have been lifesaving on Macondo but would also be relevant to other projects.

By identifying incremental processes throughout the drilling of any well, the lessons learned from Macondo—the *Process Interruption Protocol*—would allow rig leaders to apply the technique and minimize the chance of ever losing control of another well.

Questions and Answers

Throughout this written presentation, I've endeavored to recall a litany of Q&A sessions with questions coming from every direction—young engineers, service company experts, corporate executives, litigators, petroleum engineering faculty, world-class offshore drilling engineers, and, of course, a diverse cross-section of other oilfield hands and petroleum engineers from around the world. And from those questions, I've bolstered and salted my generic presentation with answers and footnotes, as appropriate, throughout.

But there are other important Q&A topics, raised in technical sessions around the world, that I'll address here.

Q&A #1—The Bladder Effect

The possible phenomenon of "the bladder effect" was apparently first debated on the rig just after 6:00 P.M. as the causal reason for the well producing 15 barrels and the drillpipe pressure not bleeding to zero (0 psi). Neither side of the debate was supported by an engineering assessment of the data.

Regardless of the *basis* of the argument for the *bladder effect* (fluid leakage through the annular, or the annular rubber being pushed deeper into the BOP by heavy mud in the riser, or a bubble of gas under the annular BOP, or whatever, whether real or imaginary), the *result* of the argument being "won" by the operator was devastating—because it caused NPT-1 to be aborted and NPT-2 to be commenced.

Here, in the spirit of the **Process Interruption Protocol**, let us allow the hypothetical *bladder effect* to become a part of the *interruptive* *data*. That means the *bladder effect*, as related to the annular BOP, would need to be resolved from an engineering perspective.

Such resolution would have been simple. To do so, recall the that NPT was a simulation. The well was kicking *only* because the annular BOP was closed around the seawater-filled drillpipe. So, to get rid of the BOP-related bladder effect, let's take the annular BOP out of the process.

A three-step procedure to take the annular BOP out of the NPT equation would give us a quick resolution: (1) Open the annular BOP, and note the well is immediately dead (1,000 psi overbalanced), and then (2) close the VBR (variable-bore ram), which contains no "bladder," and then (3) repeat the NPT pressure-reduction process through the drillpipe.

With the annular BOP (bladder) taken out of the equation, the repeated NPT through the drillpipe (using the closed VBR) would once again expose the deepest casing and annulus to the extreme drawdown (with zero chance of mud leaking down the riser).

With what result? (1) The path down the pay-zone annulus and into the wellbore would have already been flushed by the original 15 barrels of flow from the formation, (2) the well would have kicked sooner and harder (with higher flow rates), and (3) the build-up pressure would have more rapidly settled at the SIDPP (shut-in drillpipe pressure) of 1,400 psi. All of that would have led to the same conclusion, at the time—repeated here for clarity:

(1) There was a leak between the wellbore and the annulus.

(2) The problem mandatorily should have been investigated and fixed before continuation of the temporary-abandonment procedure.

Q&A #2—Casing breach below the float collar

This concept—a casing breach below the float collar—was argued in court by expert technical witnesses, each with a high incentive to win the breach/no-breach debate on behalf of his or her respective client.

Specifically—contrary to the data presented for the cement job described in **slide 8**—a claim was made that the casing had been breached (i.e., a wide-open hole in the casing) just below the float collar.

The claim was based on two technical reasons: (1) during the casing running procedure, the casing took load (increased drag) and had to be worked through the original under-reaming ledge at 18,130 feet (pictured in **slide 5**); and (2) immediately after all the casing was run (and was rigged up for cementing), it took several attempts and more than 3,000 psi to finally break circulation—which was argued as evidence that the casing had just been breached (cracked, split, jumped a box) below the (later) pressure-tested top of the float collar and the plugged guide shoe.

The counterargument was that it took 3,000 psi to clear rock debris and previously drilled cuttings from the plugged guide shoe (a rounded device installed on the bottom end of the shoe-track casing).

The crux of the argument was that—given such a breach—all the original cement would have exited the casing at the breach (rather than at the bottom of the casing) and gone up the annulus (above the breach). Further, had this been the case, there would have been no annular or shoe-track cement below the breach, leaving the bottom half of the pay zone uncemented and exposed to the open wellbore (through the wide-open breach and up through the open float collar).

There was no hard data *presented* in court to counter either argument, and the judge was left to make his decision about how to proportionally allocate shares of fault (think dollars), accordingly.

Conversely, the following assessment allows the data to speak for itself. Specifically, the Macondo well flowed 15 barrels in five minutes, before the well was shut in. Afterward, the continued flow into the low-pressure wellbore was so slow that it took thirty-five minutes (recall the pressure-buildup curve) to pressure the wellbore to the equilibrium SIDPP of 1,400 psi.

That being said, had the flow been through (into) an open casing breach adjacent to the middle of the pay zone, as claimed, with more than 1,000 psi of underbalance—one inch from the proven-high-capacity *uncemented* Macondo reservoir—the resulting kick (into the casing and up through the open float collar) would have manifested explosively fast, measured in seconds.

That did not happen.

Conversely, the actual flow path was so arduous it took thirty-five minutes for the *flowing* produced fluid to pressure-up the inside of the casing to 1,400 psi. *Arduous* in this case means hydrocarbons were flowing down through 100 feet of mud-contaminated-cement in the ¾-inch-wide annulus and then up through the mud-contaminated cement in the 180-foot-long shoe track, before flowing through the open (not-converted) float collar and into the wide-open wellbore.

Bottom line: the slow-flow-rate kick data seen in the pressure-buildup curve (**slide 14**) confirm *there was no breach in the casing below the float collar.*

Q&A #3—Spotting high-density mud in the rat hole

This would have been a zero-time, zero-dollar action. That is to say, while circulating bottoms-up after logging, just before pulling the bit for the casing job, a driller typically calls the mudroom to make a small (10-barrel) but heavy (17-ppg) mud pill. When ready, the driller flips a switch, picks up the 10-barrel pill, and counts strokes to pump it down to and out the bottom of the drillpipe before stopping the pumps, pulling the bit, and leaving the pill behind. With that simple procedure, the rat-hole gravity-segregation problem goes way.

This was not done on the Macondo well.

It's important to say here that any deep, hot, high-pressure cement job can experience problems. The Macondo production-casing cement job, as designed, had its own share of built-in *potential* problems—cement quality and set time, small cement volume, slow displacement rate, pressure-sensitive annulus, multiple workstring and casing sizes, and tight-fitting casing (7-inch casing inside an 8-1/2-inch hole). With so many *potential* problems that might affect final cement quality, one such almost-guaranteed (as opposed to *potential*) problem had an easy solution—prevention of cement contamination by spotting a heavy-mud pill in the rat hole. Without the dense mud pill, the resulting gravity-segregation began the moment the cement job was complete—long before the heavy cement (in the annulus and in the shoe track) had even the slightest chance of curing while located above the lighter-weight oil-base mud in the rat hole. (Recall earlier reference to API RP 65 Section 7.5)

Q&A #4—Use of dispersant after the blowout

Though my presentations targeted the *cause* of the blowout, months of public and media pressure about the environmental impact of the blowout increased public and industry concern across the nation and worldwide. I was asked about the Macondo dispersant during presentations at several locations, including the Evangeline (Lafayette, Louisiana) Sierra Club; Melbourne, Australia; and St. John's, Newfoundland (to name a few), which opened the door for the following answer.

BP's Macondo well flowed for 86 days and spilled 5 million barrels of crude oil. The spilled oil was "dispersed" with Corexit (produced by Nalco Holding Company) as preauthorized by the US EPA (Environmental Protection Agency) for oil spills in navigable waters. Environmental experts (including, for example, marine biologists and environmentalists from my alma mater, the University of Miami) have spoken **with vigor** against toxic, slow-acting, inefficient Corexit, and they have recommended non-toxic, faster-acting, more-efficient, enzyme-based bioremediation agents. There may be many brands, but one is OSE-II. Such products, proven around the world, don't disperse the oil; they work by causing indigenous bacteria to get very hungry for oil.

The US EPA misclassifies such products as bacteria-based (though there are no bacteria in the products) and has declared them unsuitable for oil spills in US navigable waters.

Post-Macondo hydrocarbon spills (for example, Santa Barbara County in 2015) have used and will continue to use the same ineffective and toxic Corexit dispersant unless the EPA can be convinced otherwise. For more technology-based information on this hotly debated topic, see www.ProtectMarineLifeNow.org.

Q&A #5—Macondo topics not covered herein

My point of view while studying Macondo often felt as if I were watching an autopsy by coat-and-tie attorneys who were pretending to be pathologists trying to determine not why the patient had died during a physical exam but how to allocate liability for the patient's death. And I didn't like what I saw. And I'd like to never see it again. So, I kept my assessment of Macondo simple.

Accordingly, my focus for this presentation has been on the following: (1) assessing data that define the definitive mechanical and operating steps and decisions that contributed to and *caused* the blowout, and (2) applying lessons learned from Macondo to future work.

Further, the following *additional* topics were not (could not be) included during my short verbal presentations, but they are likely of interest to a wider audience. They were not included in my presentation because none is considered to be a contributor to the *cause* of the blowout.

Each is addressed in *The Simple Truth.*

(1) drilling the Macondo pay interval below the lost-circulation zones (note: I address such geologic hazard drilling, specifically transition-zone drilling, in *The Simple Truth*, as per my 1976 [Not a typo!] SPE paper: "A Risk Analysis of Transition Zone Drilling";

(2) not circulating prudent/recommended volumes of mud to clear the wellbore before running casing;

(3) running a long string of production casing versus a liner with or without a tie-back;

(4) using nitrified cement;

(5) fluid losses recorded during the cement job;

(6) running fewer-than-recommended casing centralizers;

(7) not running a CBL (cement bond log); and

(8) other credible topics way beyond the scope of my one-hour presentation.

Additional Macondo-blowout topics not in my presentation continue to be covered in-depth by others, including (1) the highly credible "umbrella topics" listed in the text for **slide 21**, and (2) all *post-blowout* decisions, activities, and operations that occurred aboard the *Deepwater Horizon* the night of April 20, 2010, and during the subsequent months-long killing of the Macondo well.

Because I was limited to about an hour of presentation time, my apologies (though without remorse) if I left out anybody's hot-button topic(s).

Q&A #6—Post-Macondo blowouts

Though my goal for Macondo was specific relative to *cause*, I was also convinced that the assessment of the data and application of results would ultimately help the industry's entire well-management community minimize the chance of ever losing control of another well.

Maybe that has happened. It's not improbable that somebody read my book or heard my presentation and made a related decision that kept a well safe. But there's no way to ever know . . . because a well *not losing control* is the norm.

Yet in the years since BP's Macondo blowout, there have been other significant blowouts around the world. I have not researched for even a minute any of those events, which I leave to others.

I can only hope that young engineers and skilled and experienced experts alike will do the following: (1) use every academic, intellectual, common-sense, and on-the-job-training tool they have so they can manage and take responsibility for every well they're ever involved with, (2) vigorously use the **Process Interruption Protocol** procedure as appropriate, and (3) look in depth at each failure—by assessing data and applying lessons learned—always with the same goal: to minimize the chance of ever losing control of another well.

In Closing

Only if we understand and care about
the cause of BP's Macondo blowout
will we know why it should not have happened
and why it should never happen again.

Readers, especially those who have, or are studying to have, technical and operating responsibilities in the oil and gas industry, please apply the lessons learned herein throughout the rest of your career, to every well, onshore, offshore, around the world;

Further, if you have found this book useful, I hope you will encourage you colleagues to read the following:

(1) *The Simple Truth: BP's Macondo Blowout*, and

(2) *From the Podium: BP's Macondo Blowout*

Comments welcome:

John Turley at:
jatmessages@gmail.com
or to: J.A. (John) Turley on LinkedIn
Website: JohnTurleyWriter.com

ADDENDUM ONE—
Diagrams from *The Simple Truth*

The following photos and full-scale schematics are from *The Simple Truth: BP's Macondo Blowout*. Many of the *diagrams* were used (as noted) as the base drawings for slides in this presentation.

Diagram 1—(Photo) Transocean Marianas (Permission on File)
Diagram 2—Install 36-Inch Structural Casing
Diagram 3—Install 28-Inch Casing
Diagram 4—Install 22-Inch Casing
Diagram 5—Blowout Preventers
Diagram 6—Diverter System
Diagram 7—(Photo) *Deepwater Horizon*—Pre-blowout (Permission on File)
Diagram 8—Install 18-Inch Liner
Diagram 9—Well Kicks Below 18-Inch Liner
Diagram 10—Install 16-iIch Long Liner
Diagram 11—Install 13⅝-Inch, 11⅞-Inch, and 9⅞-Inch Liners
Diagram 12—Production Liner Option
Diagram 13—Liner Tie-Back Option
Diagram 14—Conversion of Float Collar
Diagram 15—Install 9⅞-Inch X 7-Inch Production Casing
   Used in Presentation Slide 4
Diagram 16—Production Casing Cement Job
   Used in Presentation Slide 5
Diagram 17—Wellhead, Hanger, and Lockdown Seal Ring

Diagram 22—Production Casing—Rat-Hole Implications

Used in Presentation Slide 8

Diagram 18—Abandonment Simulation

Used in Presentation Slides 9 and 10

Mudlogging Chart—BP's Internal Investigation, page 88 therein

Used in Presentation Slides 13, 14, 15, 29

This document was discussed in, but was not presented in, *The Simple Truth*

Diagram 19—Negative Pressure Tests

Diagram 20—Leak, Displacement, and Flow

Used in Presentation Slides 16, 17, 18

Diagram 21—(Photo) Transocean *Deepwater Horizon*— Post-blowout

Diagram 1 (Photo)
Transocean's
Transocean Marianas

Note helideck on forward starboard corner

Note Anchor lines on corners

Source & Permission on file

Diagram 2

Mississippi Canyon Block 252 #1— Macondo—*Transocean Marianas*
Install 36-inch structural casing

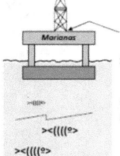

Rig Floor (RKB) at zero feet

Sea level at 75 feet RKB

Gulf of Mexico is 4,992 feet deep
at location of Macondo well

Seafloor at 5067 feet RKB

36-inch structural casing at 5,321 feet RKB

While the 36-inch casing was being jetted to its
target depth, the "drilled cuttings" (sand and
shale) spilled onto the seafloor

Note: Casing, after installation below the seafloor, is as
shown above. For reader orientation, the drilled part of the
well may be better visualized as follows:

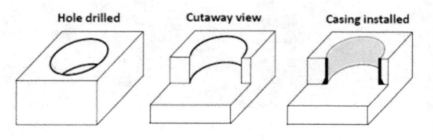

Hole drilled   Cutaway view   Casing installed

Diagram 3
Install 28-inch casing

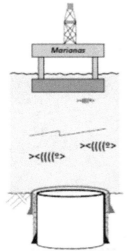

Rig Floor (RKB) at zero feet

Sea level at 75 feet RKB

Seafloor at 5067 feet

36-inch structural casing at 5,321 feet

28-inch casing at 6,217 feet

While drilling below the 36-inch casing, the drilled cuttings spilled onto the seafloor. After running the 28-inch casing, crews filled the annulus outside the casing with cement from the shoe (bottom of the casing) to the seafloor. To drill deeper, see below.

Drilling fluid (mud or seawater) pumped from the rig, down the drill string, and through the drill bit, where it mixes with drilled cuttings.

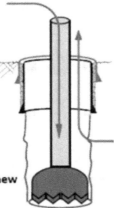

Drilling fluid and cuttings leave the bit and are pumped up the annulus, then spill onto the seafloor.

Drill bit drilling below 28" casing, preparing new hole for 22" casing

Diagram 4
Install 22-inch casing with Wellhead

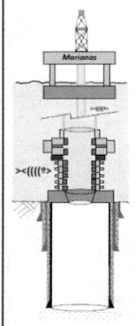

Rig Floor (RKB) at zero feet

Sea level at 75 feet RKB

Marine Riser (connects rig to blowout preventer and wellhead)

Blowout Preventers (BOPs) on top of Wellhead at 5,057 feet

Seafloor at 5,067 feet

36-inch structural casing at 5,321 feet

28-inch casing at 6,217 feet

22-inch casing at 7,937 feet, with wellhead permanently attached at 5,057 feet

While drilling below the 28" casing, the cuttings went to the seafloor. After running the 22" casing and the wellhead, the 22" casing's annulus was filled with cement from the casing shoe to the seafloor.

This critical step allowed the BOPs (18-3/4" inside diameter) to be installed on top of the wellhead, and the riser (21" outside diameter) to be installed on top of the BOPs. Note: scale of drawings is exaggerated

New drilled cuttings from below the 22" casing will be circulated up the drillpipe annulus (through rock, casing, BOP, and riser) to the rig

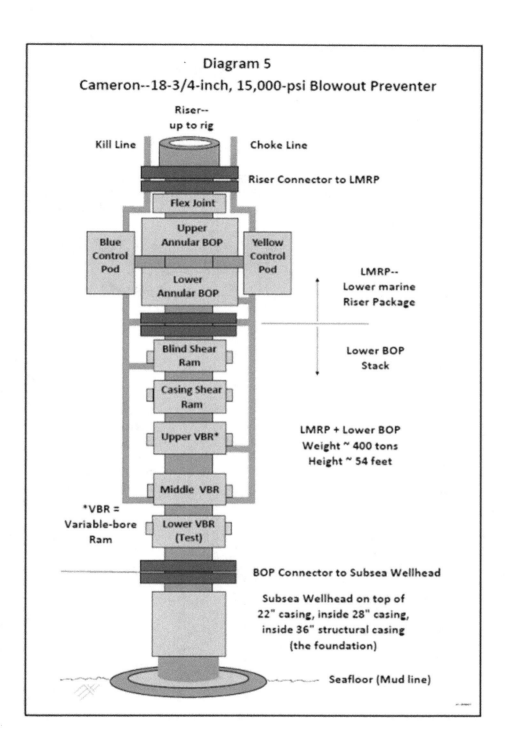

Diagram 5
Cameron--18-3/4-inch, 15,000-psi Blowout Preventer

Riser--
up to rig

Kill Line

Choke Line

Riser Connector to LMRP

Flex Joint

Upper Annular BOP

Blue Control Pod

Yellow Control Pod

Lower Annular BOP

LMRP--
Lower marine
Riser Package

Lower BOP
Stack

Blind Shear Ram

Casing Shear Ram

Upper VBR*

LMRP + Lower BOP
Weight ~ 400 tons
Height ~ 54 feet

Middle VBR

*VBR =
Variable-bore
Ram

Lower VBR
(Test)

BOP Connector to Subsea Wellhead

Subsea Wellhead on top of
22" casing, inside 28" casing,
inside 36" structural casing
(the foundation)

Seafloor (Mud line)

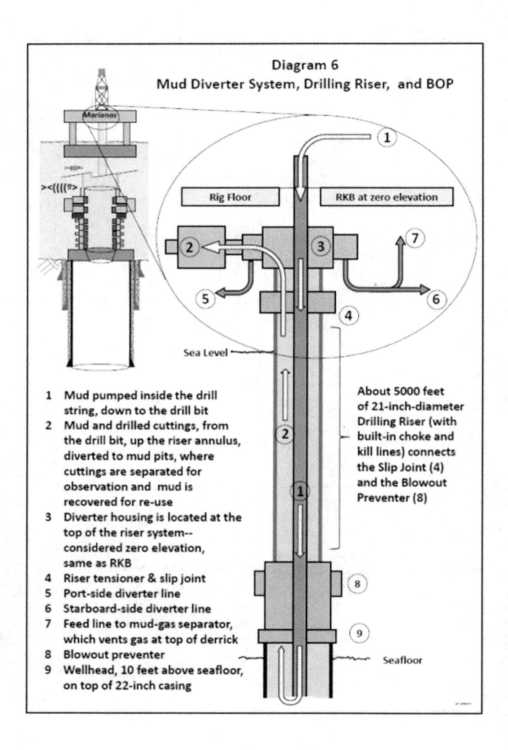

Diagram 6
Mud Diverter System, Drilling Riser, and BOP

Rig Floor

RKB at zero elevation

Sea Level

1 Mud pumped inside the drill string, down to the drill bit

2 Mud and drilled cuttings, from the drill bit, up the riser annulus, diverted to mud pits, where cuttings are separated for observation and mud is recovered for re-use

3 Diverter housing is located at the top of the riser system-- considered zero elevation, same as RKB

4 Riser tensioner & slip joint

5 Port-side diverter line

6 Starboard-side diverter line

7 Feed line to mud-gas separator, which vents gas at top of derrick

8 Blowout preventer

9 Wellhead, 10 feet above seafloor, on top of 22-inch casing

About 5000 feet of 21-inch-diameter Drilling Riser (with built-in choke and kill lines) connects the Slip Joint (4) and the Blowout Preventer (8)

Seafloor

Diagram 7 (Photo)
Transocean *Deepwater Horizon*

Note: Helideck is behind derrick (forward port corner)

Horizontal flotation columns are submerged during normal drilling operations

Source and Permission on file

Diagram 8
Install 18-inch liner

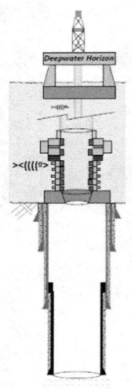

Rig Floor (RKB) at zero feet

Sea level at 75 feet RKB

Marine Riser

Blowout Preventers (BOPs) on top of
Wellhead at 5,057 feet

Seafloor at 5,067 feet

36-inch structural casing at 5,321 feet

28-inch casing at 6,217 feet

22-inch casing at 7,937 feet
with Wellhead attached

18-inch liner at 8,969 feet
(top of liner at 7,489 feet)

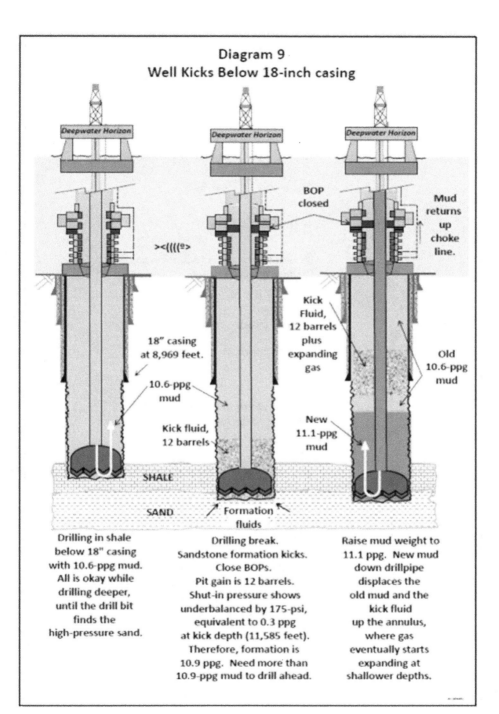

Diagram 9
Well Kicks Below 18-inch casing

BOP closed

Mud returns up choke line.

18" casing at 8,969 feet.

10.6-ppg mud

Kick fluid, 12 barrels

Kick Fluid, 12 barrels plus expanding gas

Old 10.6-ppg mud

New 11.1-ppg mud

SHALE

SAND

Formation fluids

Drilling in shale below 18" casing with 10.6-ppg mud. All is okay while drilling deeper, until the drill bit finds the high-pressure sand.

Drilling break. Sandstone formation kicks. Close BOPs. Pit gain is 12 barrels. Shut-in pressure shows underbalanced by 175-psi, equivalent to 0.3 ppg at kick depth (11,585 feet). Therefore, formation is 10.9 ppg. Need more than 10.9-ppg mud to drill ahead.

Raise mud weight to 11.1 ppg. New mud down drillpipe displaces the old mud and the kick fluid up the annulus, where gas eventually starts expanding at shallower depths.

Diagram 10
Install 16-inch long liner

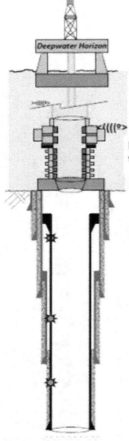

Rig Floor (RKB) at zero feet

Sea level at 75 feet RKB

Marine Riser

Blowout Preventers (BOPs) on top of
Wellhead at 5,057 feet

Seafloor at 5,067 feet

36-inch structural casing at 5,321 feet

28-inch casing at 6,217 feet

22-inch casing at 7,937 feet with
Wellhead attached

18-inch liner at 8,969 feet

16-inch "long liner" at 11,585 feet
(top of liner at 5,227 feet).
Rupture disks (☼)installed in liner at 6046,
8304, and 9560 feet as pressure-release
safety devices in case the well is a discovery
and is completed for production.

Diagram 11
Install three liners—13-5/8 and 11-7/8 and 9-7/8
(Several days between liners)

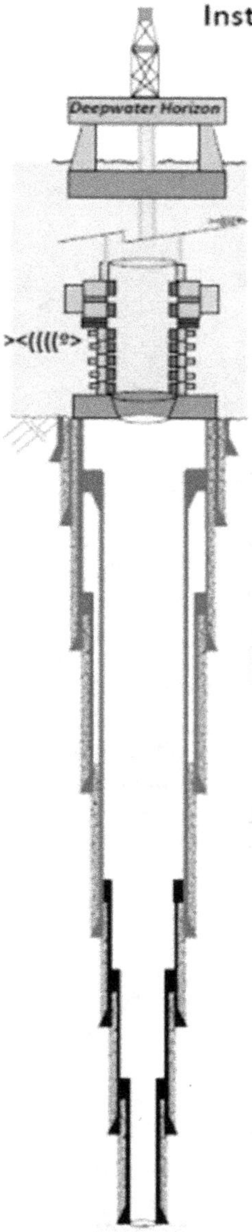
Deepwater Horizon
Rig Floor (RKB) at zero feet
Sea level at 75 feet RKB
Marine Riser
Blowout Preventers (BOPs) on top of Wellhead at 5,057 feet
Seafloor at 5,067 feet
36-inch structural casing at 5,321 feet
28-inch casing at 6,217 feet
22-inch casing at 7,937 feet with Wellhead attached
18-inch liner at 8,969 feet
16-inch long liner at 11,585 feet
13-5/8-inch liner at 13,145 feet (Top of liner at 11,153 feet)
11-7/8-liner at 15,103 feet (Top of liner at 12,803 feet)
9-7/8-inch liner at 17,168 feet (Top of liner at 14,759 feet) (Discovery Zone is below this liner)

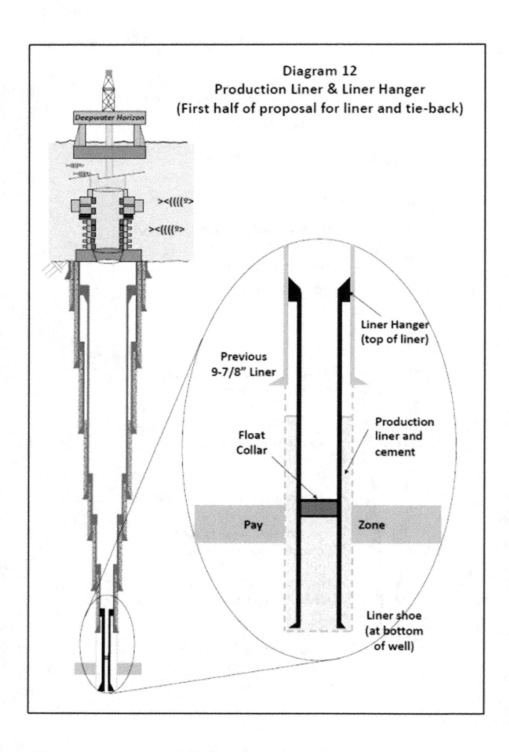

Diagram 12
Production Liner & Liner Hanger
(First half of proposal for liner and tie-back)

Deepwater Horizon

Liner Hanger (top of liner)

Previous 9-7/8" Liner

Production liner and cement

Float Collar

Pay   Zone

Liner shoe (at bottom of well)

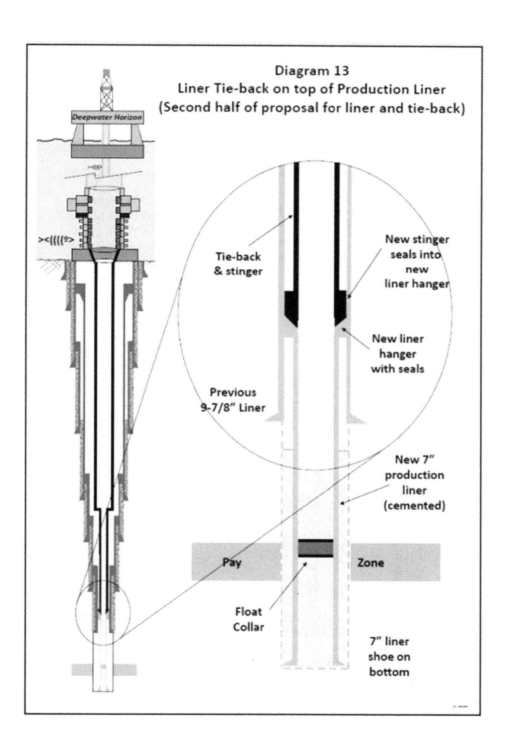

Diagram 13
Liner Tie-back on top of Production Liner
(Second half of proposal for liner and tie-back)

Tie-back & stinger

New stinger seals into new liner hanger

New liner hanger with seals

Previous 9-7/8" Liner

New 7" production liner (cemented)

Pay   Zone

Float Collar

7" liner shoe on bottom

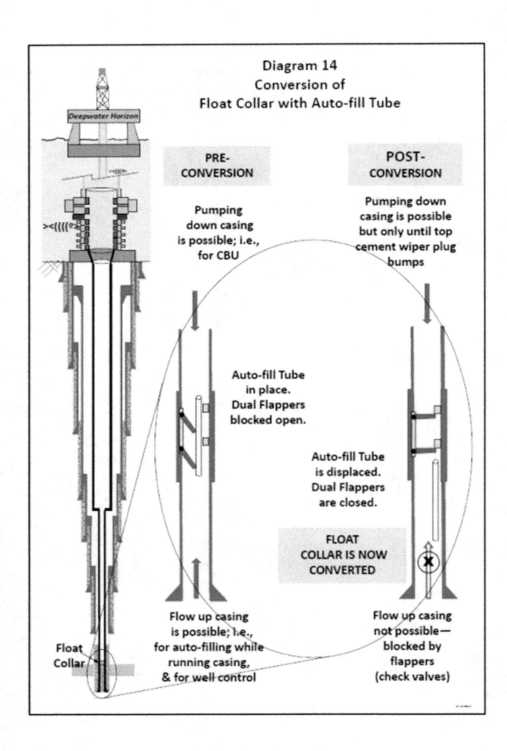

Diagram 14
Conversion of
Float Collar with Auto-fill Tube

PRE-CONVERSION

Pumping down casing is possible; i.e., for CBU

Auto-fill Tube in place. Dual Flappers blocked open.

Flow up casing is possible; i.e., for auto-filling while running casing, & for well control

POST-CONVERSION

Pumping down casing is possible but only until top cement wiper plug bumps

Auto-fill Tube is displaced. Dual Flappers are closed.

FLOAT COLLAR IS NOW CONVERTED

Flow up casing not possible—blocked by flappers (check valves)

Float Collar

Deepwater Horizon

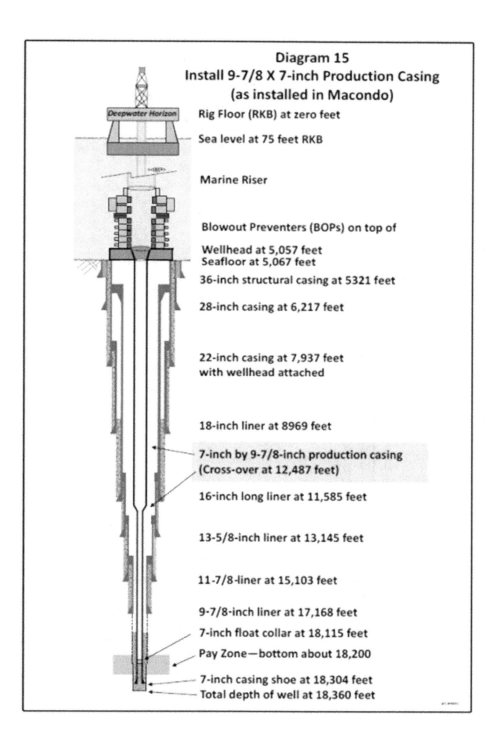

Diagram 15
Install 9-7/8 X 7-inch Production Casing
(as installed in Macondo)

Rig Floor (RKB) at zero feet

Sea level at 75 feet RKB

Marine Riser

Blowout Preventers (BOPs) on top of

Wellhead at 5,057 feet
Seafloor at 5,067 feet

36-inch structural casing at 5321 feet

28-inch casing at 6,217 feet

22-inch casing at 7,937 feet
with wellhead attached

18-inch liner at 8969 feet

7-inch by 9-7/8-inch production casing
(Cross-over at 12,487 feet)

16-inch long liner at 11,585 feet

13-5/8-inch liner at 13,145 feet

11-7/8-liner at 15,103 feet

9-7/8-inch liner at 17,168 feet

7-inch float collar at 18,115 feet

Pay Zone—bottom about 18,200

7-inch casing shoe at 18,304 feet

Total depth of well at 18,360 feet

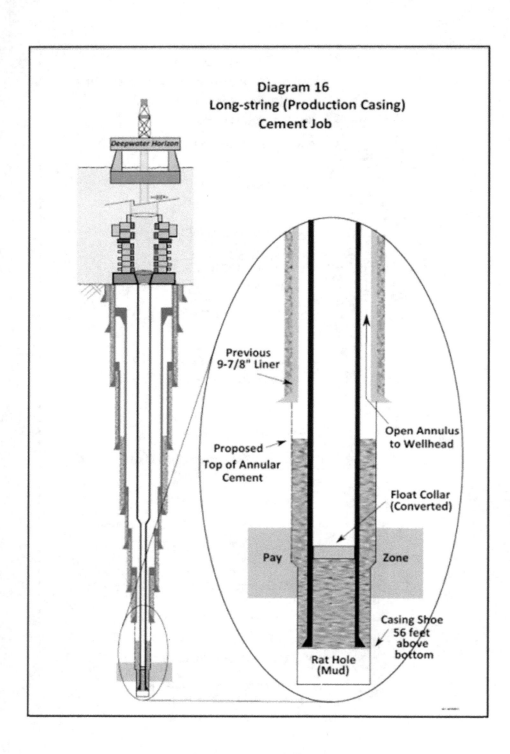

Diagram 16
Long-string (Production Casing) Cement Job

Deepwater Horizon

Previous 9-7/8" Liner

Proposed Top of Annular Cement

Open Annulus to Wellhead

Float Collar (Converted)

Pay   Zone

Casing Shoe 56 feet above bottom

Rat Hole (Mud)

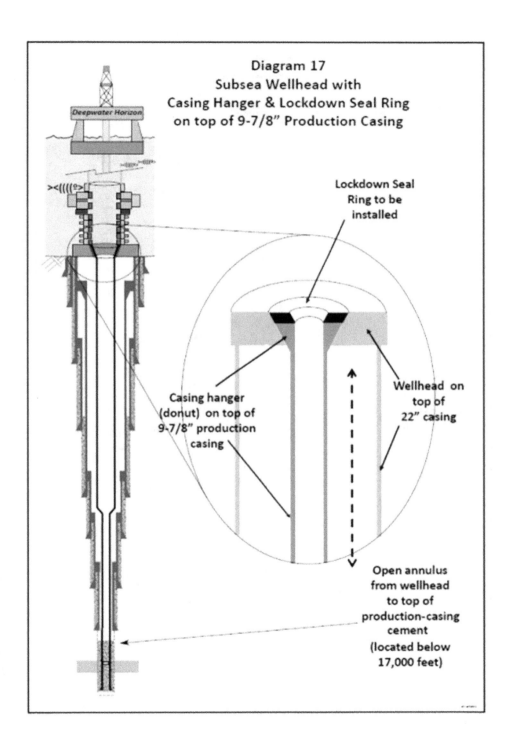

Diagram 17
Subsea Wellhead with
Casing Hanger & Lockdown Seal Ring
on top of 9-7/8" Production Casing

Lockdown Seal Ring to be installed

Casing hanger (donut) on top of 9-7/8" production casing

Wellhead on top of 22" casing

Open annulus from wellhead to top of production-casing cement (located below 17,000 feet)

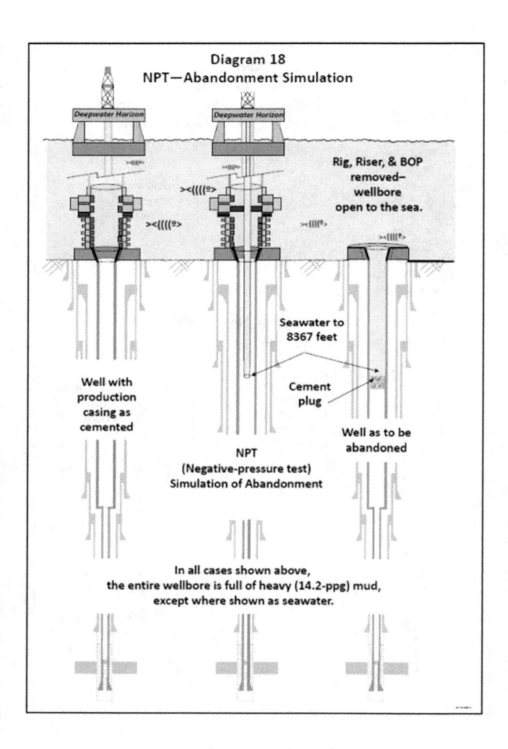

Diagram 18
NPT—Abandonment Simulation

Deepwater Horizon

Deepwater Horizon

Rig, Riser, & BOP removed— wellbore open to the sea.

Well with production casing as cemented

Seawater to 8367 feet

Cement plug

Well as to be abandoned

NPT
(Negative-pressure test)
Simulation of Abandonment

In all cases shown above,
the entire wellbore is full of heavy (14.2-ppg) mud,
except where shown as seawater.

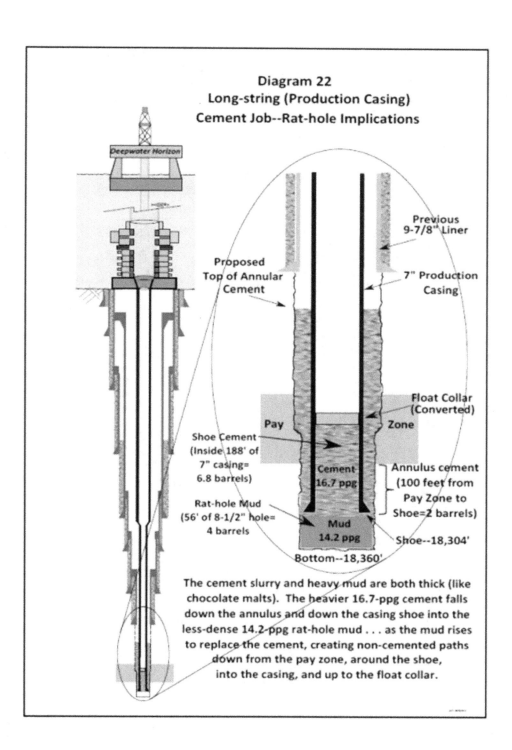

Diagram 22
Long-string (Production Casing)
Cement Job--Rat-hole Implications

Deepwater Horizon

Previous
9-7/8" Liner

Proposed
Top of Annular
Cement

7" Production
Casing

Float Collar
(Converted)

Pay   Zone

Shoe Cement
(Inside 188' of
7" casing=
6.8 barrels)

Cement
16.7 ppg

Annulus cement
(100 feet from
Pay Zone to
Shoe=2 barrels)

Rat-hole Mud
(56' of 8-1/2" hole=
4 barrels

Mud
14.2 ppg

Shoe--18,304'

Bottom--18,360'

The cement slurry and heavy mud are both thick (like
chocolate malts). The heavier 16.7-ppg cement falls
down the annulus and down the casing shoe into the
less-dense 14.2-ppg rat-hole mud . . . as the mud rises
to replace the cement, creating non-cemented paths
down from the pay zone, around the shoe,
into the casing, and up to the float collar.

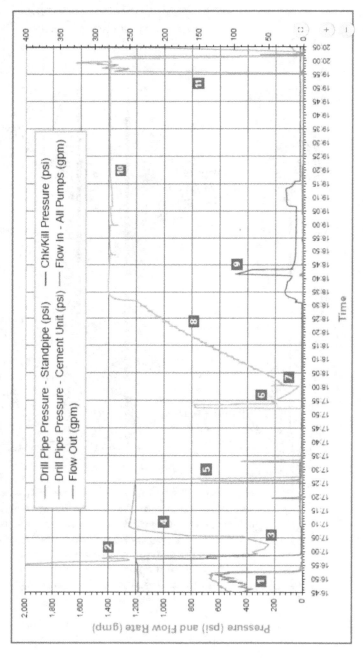

Diagram 19—NPT-1 versus NPT-2

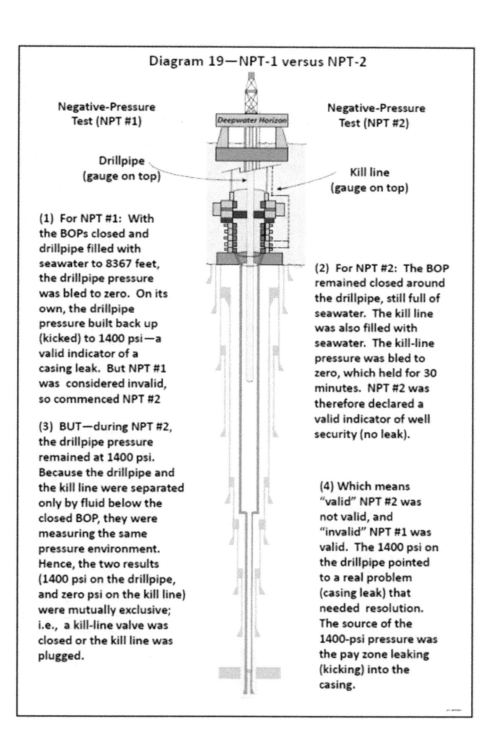

Negative-Pressure Test (NPT #1)

Negative-Pressure Test (NPT #2)

Drillpipe (gauge on top)

Kill line (gauge on top)

Deepwater Horizon

(1) For NPT #1: With the BOPs closed and drillpipe filled with seawater to 8367 feet, the drillpipe pressure was bled to zero. On its own, the drillpipe pressure built back up (kicked) to 1400 psi—a valid indicator of a casing leak. But NPT #1 was considered invalid, so commenced NPT #2

(2) For NPT #2: The BOP remained closed around the drillpipe, still full of seawater. The kill line was also filled with seawater. The kill-line pressure was bled to zero, which held for 30 minutes. NPT #2 was therefore declared a valid indicator of well security (no leak).

(3) BUT—during NPT #2, the drillpipe pressure remained at 1400 psi. Because the drillpipe and the kill line were separated only by fluid below the closed BOP, they were measuring the same pressure environment. Hence, the two results (1400 psi on the drillpipe, and zero psi on the kill line) were mutually exclusive; i.e., a kill-line valve was closed or the kill line was plugged.

(4) Which means "valid" NPT #2 was not valid, and "invalid" NPT #1 was valid. The 1400 psi on the drillpipe pointed to a real problem (casing leak) that needed resolution. The source of the 1400-psi pressure was the pay zone leaking (kicking) into the casing.

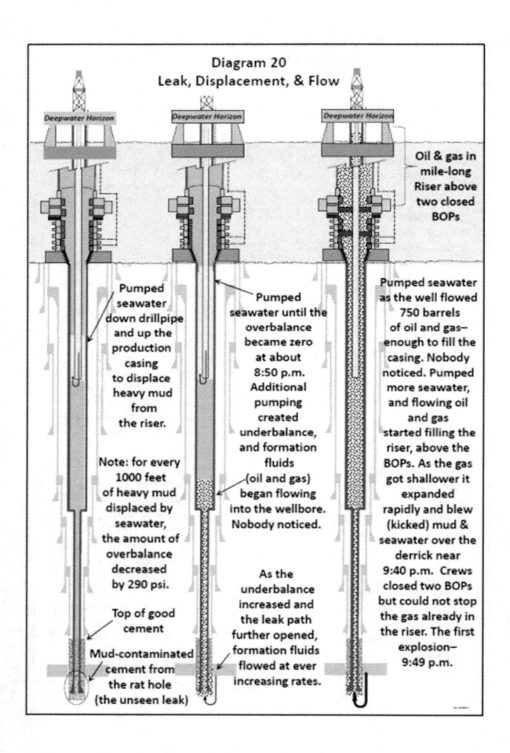

Diagram 20
Leak, Displacement, & Flow

Deepwater Horizon

Deepwater Horizon

Deepwater Horizon

Oil & gas in mile-long Riser above two closed BOPs

Pumped seawater down drillpipe and up the production casing to displace heavy mud from the riser.

Note: for every 1000 feet of heavy mud displaced by seawater, the amount of overbalance decreased by 290 psi.

Top of good cement

Mud-contaminated cement from the rat hole (the unseen leak)

Pumped seawater until the overbalance became zero at about 8:50 p.m. Additional pumping created underbalance, and formation fluids (oil and gas) began flowing into the wellbore. Nobody noticed.

As the underbalance increased and the leak path further opened, formation fluids flowed at ever increasing rates.

Pumped seawater as the well flowed 750 barrels of oil and gas—enough to fill the casing. Nobody noticed. Pumped more seawater, and flowing oil and gas started filling the riser, above the BOPs. As the gas got shallower it expanded rapidly and blew (kicked) mud & seawater over the derrick near 9:40 p.m. Crews closed two BOPs but could not stop the gas already in the riser. The first explosion— 9:49 p.m.

Diagram 21
Deepwater Horizon--21 April 2010

Photo Credits: Richard Brahm, U.S. Coast Guard, 21 April 2010

ADDENDUM TWO—

The Simple Truth:

BP's Macondo Blowout

J.A. Turley

(With minor edits for the second edition)

PROLOGUE

April 20, 2010—9:49 P.M.

Jessica Pherma's world exploded. Not the planet, but the *Deepwater Horizon*, her half-billion-dollar, drilling-rig home in the Gulf of Mexico. The event started fast, but only after hours of warnings, unheeded until too late. From under the rig an ugly growl thundered, echoed in her chest, a mere prelude to the black-geyser eruption of mud and water that blew through the rig floor and dwarfed the twenty-four-story-tall derrick.

"Shut it in!" Jessica screamed, tally book in hand, waving her arms toward the men on the rig floor, toward the deluge that threatened to drown them all. "Shut it in, now!" she yelled again.

A new noise—gas roaring from a vent line attached high in the derrick. Natural gas and atomized oil—a lethal concoction—its thick, acrid aroma unwelcome on any rig. The black cloud grew, swallowed the derrick, blanketed the rig floor. Jessica, an experienced geologist with a lifelong fire phobia, feared the worst—the end of life, a spark away.

"Open the diverter!" Earthquake-sized rumblings racked the rig and shook her body, and she wondered if the words had even left her mouth.

Men ran—some from the fury, others into the turmoil.

Jessica, too, ran. Grabbed a life vest. Slid one arm in—

A blinding fireball of reds and oranges and yellows filled the night sky, the sound and concussive force beyond movie magic. The blast—a mix of fire, steel, and hard hats—slammed her body and drove her across the deck and against a four-inch-high drainage rail. She grabbed what she could and held on tight. Eyes locked open, looking over the edge and into the abyss, all she could see was water. Black water—the sea sixty feet below. And her tally book, falling, its white wings flapping on the way down, beckoning a vision of her dad's face, framed on a white pillow in his open black casket.

Another chest-crushing blast scooted her down the rail, covered her in debris. Something heavy, metal, on her back, pushed her down. Visions of death filled her skull, oozed from pores in baking skin. With brute strength, she commanded hands, elbows, knees to take over, lever her up, free the rubble, and shake it off. Dizzy and numb, she turned to face the billowing blaze that engulfed the giant derrick as if kindling in a campfire.

Words flashed. Daddy. Death

No. Not yet. Not this horrid night. Not by fire—though the radiant heat cooking her face and penetrating her body to the core of her bones threatened to incinerate her on the spot.

More people, silhouettes, running, stumbling, in silent slow motion, away from the inferno.

Jessica stayed low. Crawled away from the edge. Away from the fire, its brutal roar growing louder, as if hungry, carnivorous, closing the distance, daring her to slow down. She found a stairwell up to the helideck. On her knees, gasping for air, she scaled first one step, then another, her own flesh and bone and blood on steel.

A wailing man, with a face she knew, stepped from the crowd, helped her up. The man, his face defined by anger and blame, grabbed her shoulders and shook hard. "You're BP," he howled. "Do *you* know what happened?"

Jessica yanked herself free, his question less important than the next minute of her life. She hugged her chest. Piercing heat attacked her back while adrenaline chills tormented her body, her torso a conflict of fire and ice. She turned as if flipped on a barbecue grill and welded her gaze onto the growing inferno consuming the rig, fifty miles from shore, perched on top of water deep enough to drown a nation, its late-night background as dark as death.

Unable to stand the heat, she turned back to the helideck crowd, her legs weak, the horizon tilting. She studied faces. Faces of men. Fewer women. Illuminated by fire. Huddled in terror. Colleagues. Acquaintances. People she hadn't met.

She wondered about missing friends—Barry, Tanker, Daylight, others. No doubt fighting the battle. Maybe their last.

Her dad. She missed him. Would miss him forever.

And Mom and Sissy. She would always love them, though they were so wrong about her dad's death.

Like last rites. Something important to say. To confess. To get off her chest.

And one more thing. The truth. *THE SIMPLE TRUTH.*

While someone bellowed commands about mustering, and lifeboat stations, and abandoning ship, she found the man who'd asked her the question. A question that deserved an answer.

"Yes," she told the man, her voice weak, her body crashing. "I know . . . *exactly* what happened."

While able crew members helped Jessica and others to lifeboats under fire-lit skies, she found her stamina increasing, driven by a passionate goal: stay alive, tell the story.

# # #
Author's note—the story is the book:
THE SIMPLE TRUTH: BP's Macondo Blowout

I hope the prologue to *The Simple Truth* got your attention. Please know there's an entire book between the prologue and the closing chapter that's about people integral to the *Deepwater Horizon*, the Macondo well, and the *cause* of the disaster. The book includes facts and data the entire industry should know, yet the story, written as narrative nonfiction, is in an easy-to read format that you, your friends, relatives, and colleagues will likely find interesting and useful.

The book is available through Amazon in hard copy and Kindle.

ADDENDUM THREE
Movie review
DEEPWATER HORIZON

By John Turley

Media reviews of the movie *Deepwater Horizon* are plentiful. But for those in the industry who truly do care, a review of such a critical movie deserves more detail; hence, the following.

I'll use a personal experience as the basis for my review.

On October 13, 2016, I joined a hundred CSM (Colorado School of Mines) petroleum engineering students and faculty for a private screening of the movie. I had been invited to emcee the event, where I watched the movie for the third time and then led an energetic hour-long discussion and Q&A session.

Every attendee had a vested interest in the career-related movie, and each was intellectually capable of understanding every aspect of what appeared on the screen.

Afterward, audience comments ranged from "OMG" and "Unbelievable" to "How could anybody have survived?" Some comments were in the form of body language only, without words to describe tear-moistened emotions. I felt the same.

We took a break, then discussed three aspects of *Deepwater Horizon:* (1) the movie, (2) the people, and (3) the technology.

The Movie

First, the entire setting, all family members, the rig hands, onshore and offshore facilities, and the massive *Deepwater Horizon* drilling rig, are exactly right. Even as the story unfolds on the rig with 126 people aboard, we get to see good renditions of the control room, shops, the galley, offices, the rig floor, a workboat, and working personnel everywhere. Then, once the disaster unfolds, with fluids—mud, oil, and gas—blowing violently over the derrick, followed by explosions and fire throughout the facility, the situation on the rig could not have been more horrific; nor could the visual effects have been more stunning, more realistic. For those who have ever been on, or who will ever be on, or who never want to be on, a drilling rig, whether onshore or offshore, the movie is a harsh view of a world we must strive to never see again.

With strong agreement among students and faculty, the bottom line for the film, as a good package of entertainment, is simply this: kudos; job well done.

The People

Also important to those who care are the relationships among the players, on several fronts. First, there's a well-portrayed rig worker (key to the story) and his wife and daughter as he prepares to go to the rig for his twenty-one-day hitch. Associated scenes do a good job of showing family dynamics and remind the audience that all persons out there, and those they leave at home, are real people with emotions and concerns and love for life.

On a different scale, the dynamics of relationships among leaders on the *Deepwater Horizon* are entirely different, albeit handled quite well in the movie. Though there are four key leadership positions on the rig (plus four visiting executives with minor roles), the conflict is simple: (1) the well belongs to BP, which pays all the bills, and BP's senior guys (*company men*) on the rig make all technical and operating decisions about the well; and (2) the rig owner, Transocean, has three senior leaders: (a) the *toolpusher*, who is in charge of the drilling rig and all its functions and personnel; (b) the *OIM*, offshore installation manager, who is responsible for the nondrilling facilities (in other words, the "hotel"); and (c) the *captain*, who is in charge of keeping the floating rig (considered by the USCG a vessel at sea) on station, hovering above the wellhead a mile below.

In a departure from reality, the movie OIM is given a major authoritarian leadership role throughout the movie, including critical rig-related matters (normally handled by the toolpusher), likely because the real-world OIM survives, while the toolpusher does not.

The rig status on the critical day is that the discovery well has been drilled, cased, and cemented. In preparation for temporary abandonment (*temporary* because it will take several years to evaluate and build the deep-water facilities), the well must be pressure tested to ensure casing and cement integrity. The high-pressure test goes well. But the negative-pressure test (designed to manually reduce the wellbore pressure to ensure there are no leaks from outside the casing) fails to prove the well is secure and generates "anomalous" data. The predominant heated-argument on screen is the following: (1) the BP leaders (company men) agree that the test data were bad but argue they were bad only because of the "bladder effect." The movie does a good job with characters arguing about the technical aspects of the bladder effect (which, in the real world, does not exist, leaving an unnecessary open issue with the audience), and (2) every other non-BP leader, even the workboat captain, argues that the test data prove the well has a leak (information they would not know) and that the BP leaders don't want to admit the failure as it would lead to a major time-and-money cement repair job. The audience does not know what's right or wrong, but by now they rank the BP rig leaders as bad guys, an apparent goal of the movie. The movie shows BP's fallback decision is to rerun the test a different way (using the kill line), which "successfully" shows the well has pressure integrity.

However, an argued one-liner in the movie proposes it's possible the second test was invalid because the kill line might have been plugged. In reality, it *was* plugged, and the second test was indeed invalid—with catastrophic results, though not mentioned again in the movie.

The falsely "successful" kill line test justifies for BP (and reluctantly for the other rig leaders, at least in the movie) the next step in the temporary-abandonment process—pumping seawater into the well to displace heavy drilling mud from the 5,000-foot-long drilling riser. Given that the well had a serious undetected casing/cement leak (a documented, albeit off-screen, failure of the company men to correctly interpret the negative-pressure test), such displacement of riser mud with seawater allowed the well to flow (also known as a kick, though unseen), even as more seawater was being pumped, exacerbating the accelerating flow.

The result was BP's Macondo blowout.

As soon as the well commences blowing out, rig personnel rightfully actuate a BOP unit (blowout preventer), but they panic verbally to one another, making the point that the BOP, in apparent total failure, does not stop the violent flow. The flow of oil and gas, like Old Faithful, finally explodes and burns, with blow-torch-like flames from the rig floor to the top of the derrick and throughout the living facilities—the cataclysm seemingly beyond belief, but very real.

Understandably, as the fire escalates, personnel conflicts go away, replaced by individual instincts for survival. The choices (well done in the movie) were few—either fight your way through the fire and get to a lifeboat or jump overboard. However, as successfully portrayed in the movie and as supported by testimony during the USCG depositions after the disaster, serious injuries were abundant, as were individual life-saving acts of heroism worthy of military-type honors.

And though the viewing audience likely will not recognize on-screen, real-life names unless they live and work on the Gulf Coast, they will have watched eleven men, played by surrogate actors in the movie, just doing their jobs, on this, their last day.

Their bodies were never found.

From the student perspective, the film vividly portrayed the importance of understanding technical concepts and data, reacting to change, respecting authority, standing up to incompetence, and accepting and executing technical job responsibilities—without fail.

The Technology

The third aspect of the hundred-minute movie that needs clarification is the necessarily rapid coverage of abundant technical issues that took place during the rig's twelve-hour countdown to disaster. A number of issues were visual only, or introduced as one-liners, requiring attendees to ponder the significance.

For example, natural gas was seen erupting on several occasions from the seafloor around the BOP, increasing in frequency and violence proportional to the tension on the screen and the ticking of the clock. Not true. No gas erupted around the wellhead either before, during, or after the blowout. Sorry to say, but this was for show, and though it successfully looked ominous, it detracted from movie credibility.

There was also a conflict about a service company leaving the rig before running a CBL, or cement bond log. Every named player on the rig (and again, even the workboat captain) was astounded that BP had released (as per the movie) the logging team without the CBL, while the BP leaders, when challenged, were confident with their decision. The concern was that the cement outside the casing at 18,000 feet (not the structural-casing cement at 5000 feet, just below the seafloor, as wrongly shown in a diagram during the movie) could be bad, and the

CBL would tell them so. Not true. The CBL does not test the cement. In reality, the tool is used in limited circumstances when there's been a significant problem during a cement job (and more so during standard completion operations). That was not the case on Macondo, where BP showed that the deep cement job, given enough time to set up, met the criteria for no CBL.

Conversely, the negative-pressure test directly tests the pressure integrity of the deep cement and the rest of the wellbore. Unfortunately, so much movie time was spent on the CBL debate that attendees were surely *wrongly* convinced that it was one of the leading causes of the blowout.

A key issue with the BOP involved the BSR (the blind shear ram). The BSR was located between two other BOP units that were closed immediately after the blowout started. Closure of the BSR was critical as part of a last-ditch emergency operation designed to release the rig from the BOP stack (to get away from the well and the source of fuel to the rig fire). But a serious consequence of the massively flowing Macondo blowout was that the drillpipe between the two closed BOP units was so severely deformed that the BSR was unable to close. The movie tempts the audience with a "big red button" that would save the day. When the red button is finally pushed (after much debate), we see sharp blades move toward one another—then stop. Consequently, the pipe is not cut, the well is not sealed, and the rig is stuck on location, burning on top of the fountain of oil and gas. There is no further mention in the movie about the BSR, other than that the BOP failed.

Summary

The CSM students in the theater were hungry for real data, wanted to understand the nuances of the one-liners, and did not want to be taken in by misinformation, all of which made for lively Q&A. And yes, because they *wanted* and *needed* to know, we thoroughly discussed "what caused the blowout," which, to be candid, was beyond the scope of the movie.

Nevertheless, though there are other technical subtopics worthy of debate, it's fair to say the *Deepwater Horizon* writers, producers, actors, and consultants did a respectable and credible job of creating dialog, building tension, revealing important issues (*even before anybody on the rig knew there was any chance of a blowout)*, and then wrapping it up with spectacular visual effects. And that takes true creativity.

Bottom line. For the movie, the people, and the technology—job well done—albeit with a few caveats.

Deepwater Horizon is a must-see movie.

ADDENDUM FOUR—
THE WHOLE TRUTH

A Novel

Published 2018

by J. A. (John) Turley

Professor Tony Zanatelli signs a summer-long contract to manage the drilling of a deep exploration well in the Gulf of Mexico. Guided by education and experience, and in spite of raging seas, raunchy geology, and tight-hole paranoia, he'll do the job well and make good money.

The project will cost millions, but hard data from the hole is the only way to know whether there's a treasure of oil and gas, or the well is a dry hole.

Regardless of results, Tony will deposit his summer salary, reunite with his wife, and share a wealth of new memories with his students.

Well—maybe.

Because the truth, the whole truth, about what resides deep in the bottom of the hole is targeted by those who will kill to prove neither life nor truth is bulletproof.

# # #

Book available through Amazon and in local bookstores through Ingram.